HOUGHTON MIFFLIN SOCIAL STUDIES

# *A*cross the Centuries

# Reading Support Workbook

 **HOUGHTON MIFFLIN**

Boston · Atlanta · Dallas · Geneva, Illinois · Palo Alto · Princeton

Printed in U. S. A.

ISBN: 0-395-94701-4

3456789-B-02 01 00 99

# Table of Contents

# Table of Contents (continued)

# Table of Contents (continued)

# Table of Contents (continued)

# Chapter Overview
## A Changing World View

**Fill in the blank spaces below with information from the chapter.**

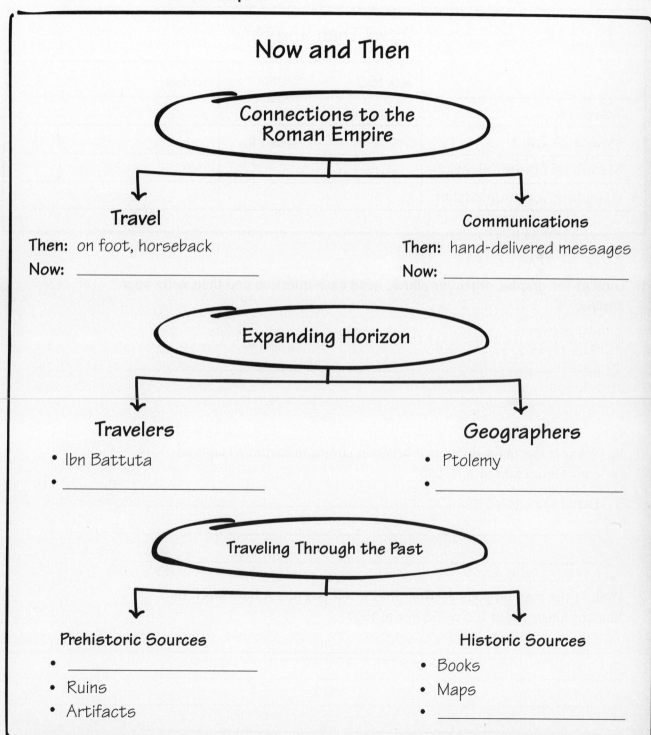

## Now and Then

**Connections to the Roman Empire**

**Travel**
Then: on foot, horseback
Now: _____

**Communications**
Then: hand-delivered messages
Now: _____

**Expanding Horizon**

**Travelers**
• Ibn Battuta
• _____

**Geographers**
• Ptolemy
• _____

**Traveling Through the Past**

**Prehistoric Sources**
• _____
• Ruins
• Artifacts

**Historic Sources**
• Books
• Maps
• _____

# CHAPTER 1
# Lesson 1 Preview
## Connections in the Roman Empire

*(Across the Centuries pp. 4–7)*

### Travel Then and Now

| | A.D. 150 | Today |
|---|---|---|
| **Travelers** | mostly traders and soldiers | all kinds of people |
| **Means of Travel** | foot, horseback, sailing ships | cars, jet planes, spacecraft |
| **Means of Communication** | messenger | electronic devices |
| **Speed of Communication** | days to months | less than one second |

1. **Look at the graphic organizer above. Read each question and then write your answer.**

   a. What were the three ways people could travel in A.D. 150?

   _____

   _____

   _____

   b. What is the main difference between communication today and communication in A.D. 150?

   _____

   _____

   _____

2. **Look at the map on page 5. What does it tell you about how much the Romans knew about the world in A.D. 150?**

   _____

   _____

   _____

CHAPTER 1

# Lesson 1 Reading Strategy
## Connections in the Roman Empire

*(Across the Centuries pp. 4–7)*

**Summarize** This reading strategy helps you remember key points about what you have read. When you get to a good break in your reading, stop and write down the main ideas of what you have read.

1. **Read page 4. What is the best summary of what the world was like for people in the Roman Empire in A.D. 150? Circle the letter next to the best answer.**

   a. People wanted to visit places like Moscow, Sydney, and Nairobi, but they couldn't get there.

   b. Because their world view was so small, the Romans did not know about cultures in Australia, the Americas, northern Asia, or Central Africa.

   c. The world is much more interesting today than it was for the people in the Roman Empire.

2. **Read the section "Travel to Foreign Lands" on page 6. Write a question you think this section would answer.**

   _____

3. **Read the section "Communication Then and Now" on pages 6–7. Write a short summary of how communication has changed since A.D. 150.**

   _____

   _____

   _____

4. **Skim through the lesson once again and fill in summaries in the chart below.**

| The World Today | The World in A.D. 150 |
|---|---|
| Travel is _____ | Travel was _____ |
| Communication is _____ | Communication was _____ |

# Lesson 1 Summary
## Connections in the Roman Empire

*(Across the Centuries pp. 4–7)*

**Thinking Focus:** How were travel and communication in the Roman Empire different from today?

## Travel Then and Now

In A.D. 150, most Romans only knew a small part of the world. That was because they did not have many ways that they could travel on land: by foot, on horseback, or in horse-drawn carts. Only government officials and traders traveled far from home. Paved roads connected most of the Roman Empire. Travel on them was slow and hard. Ocean travel was also slow. Sailors had to wait for strong winds to move their ships. Ships did not have motors or tools to help them from getting lost. Ocean travelers often starved and became sick because their ships got lost.

**?** Describe the main methods of travel within the Roman Empire in A.D. 150.

| Travel Then and Now | |
|---|---|
| **In the Roman Empire A.D. 150** | **In the United States Today** |
| On foot | By car |
| On horseback | By train |
| In a horse-drawn cart | By airplane |
| By ship with oars or sails | On a ship with an engine |

*Summary continues on next page*

Reading Support Resources

## Communication Then and Now

Communication was very slow in the Roman Empire. Messages could only be sent one way—they were carried by hand. Messengers on foot could travel about 25 miles per day. The Romans also had a postal service. The mail was carried in horse-drawn carts. These carts could only go about 100 miles in 24 hours.

Today people have many ways to send messages. Unlike in Roman times, no one has to travel to send a message. The world of **electronic communication** has changed the way information is sent from place to place. Fax machines, the Internet, and communication **satellites** can send messages around the world in just a few seconds. The Romans thought their world was huge. Today the world feels smaller. Advances in travel and communication can bring people together even if they live far away from one another.

[?] How has communication changed since A.D. 150?

**electronic communication**
(ĭ-lĕk-trŏn´ĭk kə-myōō´nĭ-kā´shən)

communication tools such as the fax, Internet, telephone, television, and computer that have cut down on the time it takes to send a message

**satellite**
(săt´l-īt´)

a manmade object that circles the earth and is often used for sending information

**CHAPTER 1**
# Lesson 2 Preview
## The Expanding Horizon
*(Across the Centuries pp. 10–15)*

### Advances in Travel

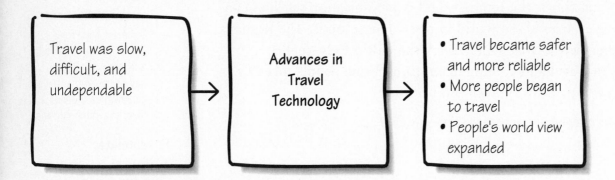

1. **Look at the graphic organizer above. Read each sentence and then fill in the blank.**

   a. Describe what traveling was like before the advances in travel technology.

   _____

   _____

   b. What was one of the results of the advances in travel technology?

   _____

   _____

2. **Look at the picture and read the text on page 14. How can advances in travel make a mapmaker's work better?**

   _____

   _____

   _____

   _____

   _____

   _____

**CHAPTER 1**

# Lesson 2 Reading Strategy
## The Expanding Horizon

*(Across the Centuries pp. 10–15)*

**Sequence** This reading strategy helps you follow the order of events. As you read, pay attention to the dates and times, as well as to words such as *before, finally, after,* and *then.*

1. **Read from the heading "Merchants, Soldiers, Explorers, Pilgrims" on page 11 up to the blue heading "Explorers" on page 12. Place the following events in order by writing 1, 2, and 3 in the blanks.**

   ____ The Chinese make rigid metal stirrups.

   ____ The Romans invent iron horseshoes.

   ____ The bit is developed in the Middle East.

2. **Read the section "Explorers" on pages 12–13. Put the following events in the order they happened in history.**

   ____ The lateen sail was invented.

   ____ The Chinese began using the sternpost rudder.

   ____ The Chinese began using the magnetic compass.

3. **Read the section "Early Maps" on page 15. Write down all the words or phrases that give you clues to the sequence of events.**

   _____

   _____

4. **Read through the whole chapter once again. Complete the timeline with events and dates from your reading.**

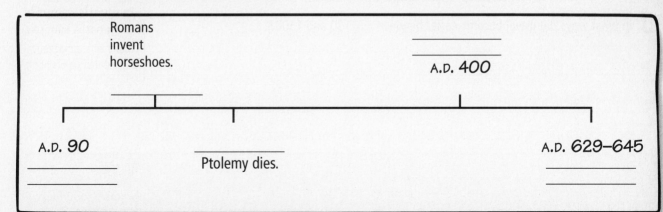

# Lesson 2 Summary
## The Expanding Horizon

*(Across the Centuries* pp. 10–15)

**Thinking Focus:** How and why did people travel in the years between A.D. 150 and 1500?

## Merchants, Soldiers, Explorers, Pilgrims

Starting about 100 B.C., merchants in the Middle East used camels to move their goods to sell. Camels could carry up to 1,100 pounds on their backs. They could work in extreme heat and cold. Often merchants would tie their camels together in **caravans** on their long journeys. Soldiers and others who needed to move more quickly rode horses. Three inventions made horseback riding easier and faster: the **stirrup,** the bit, and the horseshoe. Stirrups and bits gave riders more control over their horses. Horseshoes protected the animal's feet.

Travel by ship during this time was often very dangerous. Boats were not well built, and could be upset by bad weather. Sailors had to depend on wind to move their boats. Three inventions made ocean travel easier and safer. The **lateen sail** made it less difficult to sail in any direction, no matter which way the wind blew. The **sternpost rudder** let sailors steer their boats more easily. And the **magnetic compass** helped sailors keep their ships going in the right direction.

As transportation improved, more people began to travel and write about their adventures. Xuanzang was a Chinese pilgrim who visited India to collect Buddhist teachings. He later wrote wonderful stories about his journey. Another traveler and writer, Ibn Battuta, visited Arabia, Asia, Africa, and Spain. Mapmakers used information from travelers such as these to keep their maps up to date.

**?** In what ways did travel become easier between A.D. 150 and 1500?

**caravan**
(kăr′ə-văn′)

a group of pack animals traveling in single file to get to a place

**stirrup**
(stŭr′əp)

loops on either side of a saddle that help a rider get on and stay on

**lateen sail**
(lə-tēn′sāl)

a sail in the shape of a triangle

**sternpost rudder**
(stûrn′pōst′ rŭd′ər)

a paddle under a ship that is used to help steer the boat

**magnetic compass**
(măg-nĕt′ĭk kŭm′pəs)

a tool with a magnetic needle that points north

*Summary continues on next page*

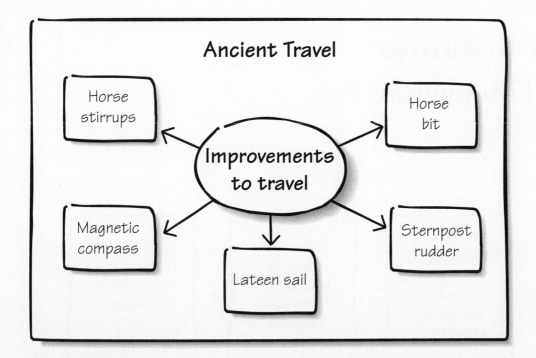

## Early Maps

Travelers and explorers brought home a great deal of information about the world. Mapmakers used this new knowledge to make their maps better. The greatest mapmaker in the Roman Empire was Ptolemy. He made one of the best maps of the world as it was known to the Romans in 150. Later, as the Roman Empire declined, Ptolemy's maps were not used in Europe. For the next 1,000 years, European maps gave a false view of the world. The most common European maps were called T-O maps. They showed the continents of Europe, Asia, and Africa separated by bodies of water. Together, these formed a "T." The ocean, which was the "O," surrounded the three continents.

Ptolemy's maps continued to be well-known and used in the Muslim world. European map makers fell behind. But many people in the East still studied Ptolemy. As a result, people in the Muslim world invented new tools that helped explorers find their way more easily. Many years later, this information was brought to Europe.

? How did travelers and explorers change people's view of the world?

CHAPTER 1

# Lesson 3 Preview
## Traveling Through the Past

(*Across the Centuries* pp. 16–19)

### What Historians Do

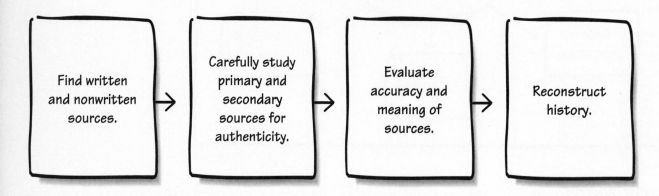

Find written and nonwritten sources. → Carefully study primary and secondary sources for authenticity. → Evaluate accuracy and meaning of sources. → Reconstruct history.

1. **Look at the graphic organizer above. Read each sentence and then fill in the blank.**

   a. What is the main idea shown in the graphic organizer?

   _____

   _____

   b. After historians find their sources and make sure the sources are authentic, what happens next?

   _____

   _____

2. **Look at all the pictures on pages 16–19 and read the captions. What do these pictures tell you about what you will learn in this chapter?**

   _____

   _____

   _____

   _____

   _____

   _____

CHAPTER 1

# Lesson 3 Reading Strategy
## Traveling Through the Past

(*Across the Centuries* pp. 16–19)

**Self-Question** This reading strategy helps you stay focused on what you read. Ask yourself questions before you read a section. Then read to see if you can find the answer to your questions.

1. **Read the red heading "Studying the Past" and the blue headings under it on page 17. Which question below do you expect to have answered in the paragraphs that follow this heading? Circle the letter next to the best answer.**

    a. What tools help historians figure out what happened many years ago?

    b. What is life like in other places around the world today?

    c. Will people be able to live in outer space in the future?

2. **Read the section "Studying the Past" to see if the question you chose was answered. If it was, write the answer to the question.**

    _____

    _____

3. **Read the red heading "Interpreting the Past" and the blue heading "Differing Views of the Past" on page 18. Which question below would you expect to have answered in the paragraphs that follow these headings?**

    a. Why do people study history?

    b. Is history the same for all people who live through it?

    c. Why can prehistory be studied only through secondary sources?

4. **Fill in the chart below by writing a question about each word in column 1. Read the lesson to find the answers to your questions.**

| Archaeology | Question: _____ |
| | Answer: _____ |
| Prehistory | Question: _____ |
| | Answer: _____ |
| The Aztec | Question: _____ |
| | Answer: _____ |

# Lesson 3 Summary
## Traveling Through the Past

*(Across the Centuries* pp. 16–19)

**Thinking Focus:** How do historians reconstruct the past?

## Studying the Past

**History** is a record of past human events. Historians study non-written sources like fossils, ruins, and artifacts. They also use written sources such as scrolls, tablets, objects with writing on them, calendars, maps, letters, and books. Historians use information from these sources and what they already know to help them understand the past. They judge whether these sources are factually correct.

A large part of human history happened before there was any writing system. To study that period, called **prehistory,** historians have to depend on ruins, fossils, and artifacts for clues and information. **Archaeology** is the study of these items. Artifacts left by past cultures often tell just as much as written material could.

Writing was first developed around 3200 B.C. in the Middle East. Written sources are divided into two types: primary sources and secondary sources. **Primary sources** are written by people who took part in, or observed an event. **Secondary sources** are written after an event, usually with the help of some primary sources. Historians like to use primary sources because people who were present at an event can usually describe it factually.

**?** Explain the difference between primary and secondary sources.

**history**
(hĭs′tə-rē)
a record of the past

**prehistory**
(prē-hĭs′tə-rē)
history that happened before writing was invented

**archaeology**
(är′kē-ol′ə-jē)
the study of the ruins, fossils, and items of past human life and culture

**primary source**
(prī′měr′ē sôrs)
a historical record of an event written by someone who actually lived through or saw the event

**secondary source**
(sĕk′ən-děr′ē sôrs)
a historical record written after an event

*Summary continues on next page*

Reading Support Resources

## Historical Sources

| Nonwritten Sources | Written Sources |
| --- | --- |
| Fossils | Maps |
| Bones | Calendars |
| Ruins | Letters |
| Artifacts | Books |

## Interpreting the Past

It is not always easy for historians to know the truth about the past. Historians must be good detectives. They must look for clues. They must ask questions about who wrote each source. They need to check every source to make sure that the picture that develops of the past is true.

Historians must also decide if the source's point of view is truthful and factual. For example, people on opposite sides of a war would have very different things to say about that war. Historians must also be judges. They must choose among different stories about the past. History is always changing as new information is discovered and studied.

**?** How do historians evaluate the accuracy of their sources?

Hale Middle School

# Chapter Overview
## Empires of the Ancient World

Fill in the blanks below with accomplishments
from each culture.

| **When:** |
| 27 B.C. – A.D. 1453 |
| **Where:** |
| Europe, Asia, North Africa |

## Empires of the Ancient World

### The Roman Empire

Achievements: _____

_____

_____

### Acquainted Cultures

Achievements of
the Sassanid Empire: _____

_____

Achievements of
the Gupta Dynasty: _____

_____

Achievements of
the Han Empire: _____

_____

_____

### The Byzantine Empire

Achievements: _____

_____

_____

CHAPTER 2

# Lesson 1 Preview
## The Fall of the Roman Empire

(*Across the Centuries* pp. 26–31)

### The End of Ancient Rome

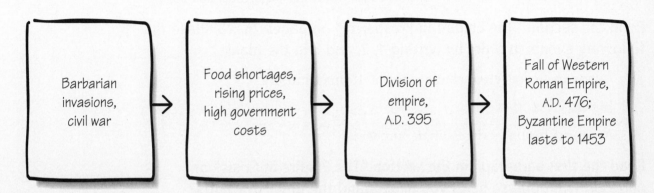

1. **Look at the graphic organizer above. Read each question and then write your answer.**

   a. What happened to the Roman Empire after the barbarian invasions and civil war?

   _____

   b. When was the fall of the Western Roman Empire?

   _____

   c. In what year did the Byzantine Empire fall?

   _____

2. **Look at the map on page 27 of your text. Then answer the following questions.**

   a. What is the title of the map?

   _____

   b. Which Germanic peoples were part of Britain?

   _____

   c. What Germanic people were in Rome?

   _____

**CHAPTER 2**

# Lesson 1 Reading Strategy
## The Fall of the Roman Empire

(*Across the Centuries* pp. 26–31)

**Sequence** This reading strategy helps you follow the order of events. As you read, pay attention to dates and times, as well as to words such as *before*, *finally*, *after*, and *then*.

1. Read the section "The Empire in Prosperity" on pages 26–28. Place the following events in order by writing 1, 2, and 3 in the blanks.

   ___ Augustus makes great changes to the Roman Empire.

   ___ Julius Caesar dies.

   ___ Augustus becomes the Roman emperor.

2. Read the first paragraph in the section "The Empire in Crisis" on page 28. What phrase helps you understand the order of events?

   _____

3. Read the rest of the section "The Empire in Crisis" on pages 28–30. Write at least two phrases that help you understand the order of the events.

   _____

   _____

4. Read the section "The Empire in Transition" on pages 30–31 through to the end of the lesson. Complete the timeline below with dates and events.

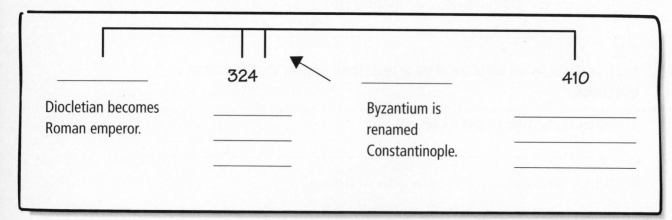

Diocletian becomes Roman emperor.   324   _____   Byzantium is renamed Constantinople.   410

# Lesson 1 Summary
## The Fall of the Roman Empire

*(Across the Centuries pp. 26–31)*

**Thinking Focus:** What led to the collapse of the Western Roman Empire?

## The Empire in Prosperity

The first Roman emperors were Caesar and Augustus. They made the Roman Empire larger by taking over land along the Rhine and Danube rivers. The Roman emperors after Augustus went on to conquer more lands. These lands were turned into **provinces** of Rome. Rome allowed the people in the provinces to go on living as they had before. But now they had to obey Roman laws and pay taxes to Rome.

The provinces provided food and protection for Rome. Roads were built to connect the provinces to Rome. The Romans also built aqueducts to provide water to their people. For a long time there was peace.

[?] Describe the relationship between Rome and its provinces.

**province**
(prŏv´ĭns)

in the Roman Empire, lands outside of Italy that were ruled by Romans

**barbarian**
(bär-bâr´ē-ən)

in the Roman Empire, people who lived along the Empire's central and eastern borders

## The Empire in Crisis

Tribes of Germanic people that the Romans called **barbarians** lived along the empire's edges. Some barbarians lived peacefully with the Romans. They traded with Rome and joined the Roman army. But other barbarian groups were not friendly to Rome.

In the late 300s, some barbarian tribes asked Rome for protection. They were afraid of the Huns, who were fierce warriors from central Asia. In order to escape the Huns, large numbers of barbarians crossed the border into the Roman Empire. Among them were some barbarians who did not like the Romans.

At the same time, Roman generals also fought for control of the government. Backed by their armies, they fought battles. They ruined the land, making food expensive and hard to get. These two things started to weaken the Roman Empire.

[?] Support this statement: The barbarians were both allies and enemies of the Romans.

*Summary continues on next page*

## The Empire in Transition

Diocletian became the Roman emperor in 284. He tried to solve some of the empire's problems. He decided to make the empire easier to defend and rule. He split the empire in two. He put two leaders in charge of the eastern empire, and two in charge of the western empire. He made the Roman army bigger. These changes cost money. This made the Roman economy weaker.

Constantine was emperor after Diocletian. He tried to make the eastern empire stronger by giving it a new capital city, Constantinople. Constantinople was a perfect location. The city had water on three sides and the Balkan Mountains on the fourth. This made it difficult for enemies to attack. Its location also made the city a perfect stopping place for merchants traveling to Europe and the East Indies. This Eastern Roman Empire, called the Byzantine Empire, lasted for 1,000 years. The Western Roman Empire got weaker. In 410, barbarian invaders raided Rome. In 476, the Western Roman Empire came to an end.

**?** What did Diocletian do to strengthen the empire?

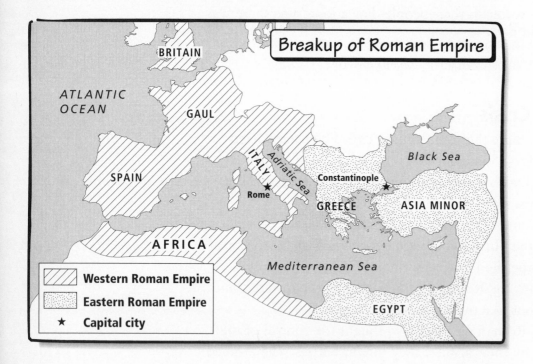

Breakup of Roman Empire

CHAPTER 2

# Lesson 2 Preview
## Acquainted Cultures

(*Across the Centuries* pp. 32–37)

| Contact Between Europe and Asia | | | |
|---|---|---|---|
| | Sassanid Persia | Gupta India | Han China |
| **Trade Partners** | China, India, Roman Empire | China, Persia, Roman Empire, S.E. Asia | India, Persia, central Asia, Roman Empire |
| **Enemies** | Huns, Roman Empire | Huns | Huns and other tribes |

1. **Look at the graphic organizer above. Then read the following sentences and fill in the blanks.**

   a. Which group was an enemy of Sassanid Persia, Gupta India, and Han China?

   _____

   b. Which group was a trade partner of Sassanid Persia, Gupta India, and Han China?

   _____

2. **Look at the map on pages 36–37. What two empires make up China?**

   _____

   _____

   _____

   _____

   _____

   _____

   _____

**CHAPTER 2**

# Lesson 2 Reading Strategy
## Acquainted Cultures

(*Across the Centuries* pp. 32–37)

**Using the Visuals** This reading strategy asks you to use photographs, maps, charts, and illustrations to help you understand what you read. As you read, be sure to study the visuals and carefully read the captions.

1. Look at the photograph on page 32 and read the caption. Write a sentence about what you can tell about the picture.

   _____

2. Study the timeline on page 33. What happened in China in A.D. 105?

   _____

3. Look at the map on pages 36–37. What group invaded the Sassanid Empire of Persia, the Gupta Empire of India, and the Western Roman Empire?

   _____

   _____

4. Now read through the whole lesson. Create a visual of your own by filling in the chart as you read each section.

| Sassanid Persia | Gupta India | China |
|---|---|---|
| Roads were: | Inventions and Discoveries: | Trade: |
| _____ | _____ | _____ |
| _____ | _____ | _____ |
| _____ | _____ | _____ |
| _____ | _____ | _____ |

# Lesson 2 Summary
## Acquainted Cultures

*(Across the Centuries pp. 32–37)*

**Thinking Focus:** In what ways did the peoples from various cultures benefit from their contact with each other?

## Sassanid Persia

For years the Roman Empire and Persia were at war with each other. Both wanted control of Armenia, an area that could give them each protection from invaders. Persia was ruled by the Sassanid **dynasty**. The Persians were good fighters. They wore armor and fought on horseback.

The trade routes that joined Rome, India, and China all ran through Persia. The Persians made sure that the roads were kept in good condition, made safe by soldiers, and had places to rest along the way. Persia also had a single system of money, which made it easy for travelers. Trade made Persia rich. It also helped Persians to learn many things from other cultures.

> **dynasty**
> (dĭ′nə-stē)
> a ruling family that lasts over a period of many years

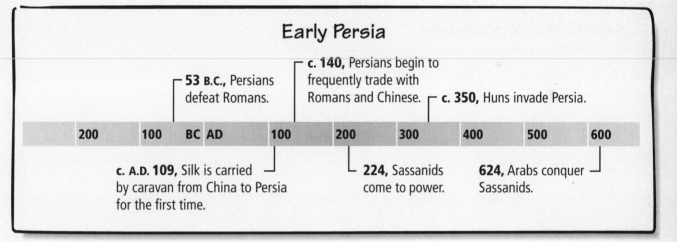

**Early Persia**

- 53 B.C., Persians defeat Romans.
- c. 140, Persians begin to frequently trade with Romans and Chinese.
- c. 350, Huns invade Persia.

| 200 | 100 | BC | AD | 100 | 200 | 300 | 400 | 500 | 600 |

- c. A.D. 109, Silk is carried by caravan from China to Persia for the first time.
- 224, Sassanids come to power.
- 624, Arabs conquer Sassanids.

[?] How did Persia become a wealthy trading nation?

*Summary continues on next page*

# Gupta India

The Gupta dynasty ruled India from A.D. 300 to 467. Like Persia, India had a strong economy and rich trade. The roads were good. People from other places could come and go easily. The arts and sciences were very important during the Gupta dynasty and the Indians shared their knowledge with others.

In 480 Hun invasions started to weaken India. By 525 the Huns had taken over India. They ruled over the Indian people for the next 200 years.

**[?]** In what ways did India's culture benefit from the prosperity that existed between 300 and 500?

# China

To the east of India was China. Its main trade route to India, Persia, and Rome was called the Silk Road. The Chinese traded their silk and gold for many things, including glass, pearls, grapes, beans, nut trees, and horses. Missionaries from India brought the religion of Buddhism to the Chinese. Like India, China also had trouble with the Huns. Emperors in the Chinese Han dynasty fought long wars against them. By 220 the Han dynasty had lost control of China. Huns and other invading tribes fought for control of the country. And so, for the next 300 years China was not united.

**[?]** What were some of the goods China traded? What are some of the goods they obtained in exchange for these items?

CHAPTER 2

# Lesson 3 Preview
## The Rise of the Byzantine Empire

(*Across the Centuries* pp. 42–45)

The Byzantine Empire

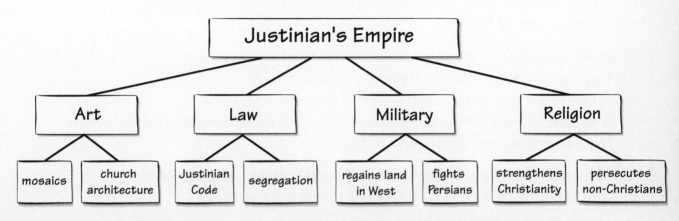

1. **Look at the graphic organizer above. Then read the following sentences and fill in the blanks.**

   a. What was the law of Justinian's empire called?

   _____

   b. What empire did Justinian's army fight against?

   _____

2. **Look at the pictures on pages 42–45. What do they tell you about the Byzantine Empire?**

   _____

   _____

   _____

   _____

   _____

   _____

   _____

CHAPTER 2

# Lesson 3 Reading Strategy
## The Rise of the Byzantine Empire

(*Across the Centuries* pp. 42–45)

**Evaluate** This reading strategy helps you recognize the difference between facts and opinions. A fact is something that can be proven to be true. An opinion is a belief based on what a person thinks or feels.

1. **Read the introduction on page 42 above the heading "Byzantine History and Culture." Which statement below is a fact?**

   a. A riot broke out in Constantinople in January 532.

   b. A woman should not be daring among men or assert herself boldly.

   c. Now is a poor time for flight.

2. **Read from the heading "Byzantine History and Culture" on page 42 to the bottom of page 43. Which statement below is an opinion?**

   a. The Romans destroyed Judaea in A.D. 70.

   b. The Hagia Sophia contains mosaics.

   c. The dome of the Hagia Sophia is awe inspiring.

3. **Read the first sentence of the section titled "A New Empire" on page 45. Is Justinian's statement that the West had been lost because of laziness a fact or an opinion? Explain your answer.**

   _____

   _____

4. **Read the section "The Persian Threat" on page 45. Then fill out the chart with two facts from what you read and two of your own opinions about what you read.**

   | Facts from Text | My Own Opinions |
   |---|---|
   |  |  |
   |  |  |
   |  |  |

# Lesson 3 Summary

## The Rise of the Byzantine Empire

*(Across the Centuries* pp. 42–45)

Summary also on
Audiotape

---

**Thinking Focus:** What were some of the accomplishments of the Byzantine Empire?

## Byzantine History and Culture

The Byzantine Empire lasted more than 1,000 years. During that time its borders changed many times. But the empire was held together by the state religion, Christianity. Byzantine Christians thought that the Emperor was God's representative on Earth, and they forced their religion on others.

The Emperor Justinian treated people who believed in other religions very badly. For example, he did not allow Jews to build temples or be part of city life. He made them become Christians. He had Jews killed. As a result, many left the empire.

The Emperor Justinian wanted art to reflect Christianity. In the capital city of Constantinople, he paid artists to make works of religious art, including many **mosaics.** Justinian hired people to build beautiful churches. One of these churches was the Hagia Sophia, the most important religious building in the empire.

**mosaic**
(mō-zā′ĭk)

a picture or design made from small pieces of colored glass stuck in plaster

Justinian also wanted to organize the old Roman laws. His new system was called Justinian's Code. It gave more rights to women, children, and slaves. It also called for a harder punishment for those who did not obey the law. The new laws were very successful. In fact, many other countries later used Justinian's Code as a model for their own legal systems.

**?** What distinctive elements of Byzantine culture developed under Justinian's rule?

Hale Middle School

*Summary continues on next page*

## Justinian Code of Law

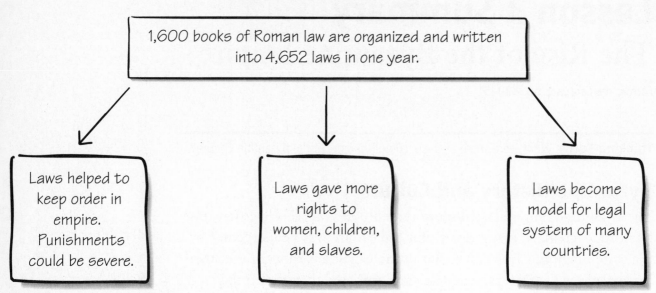

1,600 books of Roman law are organized and written into 4,652 laws in one year.

Laws helped to keep order in empire. Punishments could be severe.

Laws gave more rights to women, children, and slaves.

Laws become model for legal system of many countries.

## The Persian Threat

The Byzantine Empire was a center of **commerce**, or trade, until 1453. But the Byzantine Empire was attacked often by barbarian tribes. The real threat to the empire, however, came from the Persians. For 500 years the Byzantines and Persians fought with each other for the control of Armenia and other parts of this region. Both countries became weak from fighting all the time. Finally neither country could defend itself from new invaders.

**commerce**
(kŏm′ərs)
the buying and selling of goods

**?** How did the constant battling between Byzantium and Persia affect the two empires?

# Chapter Overview
## The Roots of Islam

**Fill in the blanks below with information from the chapter.**

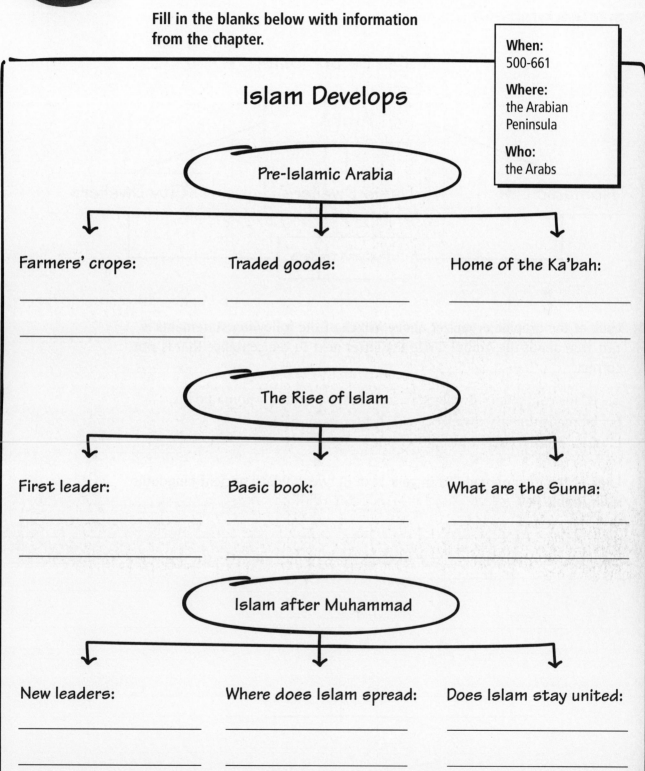

Islam Develops

**When:**
500-661

**Where:**
the Arabian Peninsula

**Who:**
the Arabs

Pre-Islamic Arabia

Farmers' crops:

_____

_____

Traded goods:

_____

_____

Home of the Ka'bah:

_____

_____

The Rise of Islam

First leader:

_____

_____

Basic book:

_____

_____

What are the Sunna:

_____

_____

Islam after Muhammad

New leaders:

_____

_____

Where does Islam spread:

_____

_____

Does Islam stay united:

_____

_____

CHAPTER 3
# Lesson 1 Preview
## Desert Bloom—Caravan Cities
*(Across the Centuries pp. 52–57)*

Arabia Before Islam

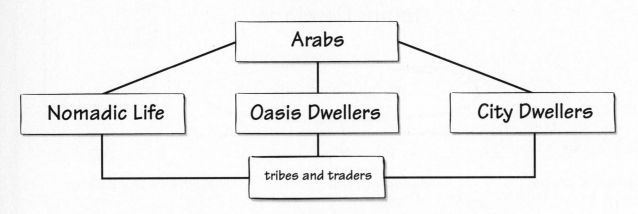

1. **Look at the graphic organizer above. Which of the following statements is <u>not</u> true about the Arabs? Circle the letter next to the sentence that is <u>not</u> correct.**

   a. Arabs can be city dwellers, oasis dwellers, or live a nomadic life.
   b. Nomads are city dwellers.
   c. City dwellers are traders.

2. **Look at the map on page 53 in your text. Between which ancient kingdoms does Arabia lie?**

   _____

   _____

CHAPTER 3

# Lesson 1 Reading Strategy
## Desert Bloom—Caravan Cities

*(Across the Centuries pp. 52–57)*

**Cause and Effect** This reading strategy helps you understand events and why they occur. As you read, think about the factors that caused an event. Then think about what the effects of that event may be.

1. Read the section "At an Oasis" on pages 53 and 55. What caused the destruction of the settlement of Ubar? Circle the letter next to the best answer.
   a. Many people came there to trade incense.
   b. The city's underground water system collapsed.
   c. Families of nomads were attracted to oases.

2. Read the section "Nomadic Life" on page 55. What was one of the effects of water and grazing land being scarce in Arabia? Circle the letter next to the best answer.
   a. Feuds over grazing or land rights would sometimes occur.
   b. Jews and Christians settled in Arabia.
   c. The nomads believed in a number of nature spirits.

3. Read the section "Towns and Trade" on page 56. What was one of the effects of traders crossing the desert?

   _____

   _____

4. Read the section "The Holy City of Mecca" on page 57. Then fill out the chart below.

| Cause | Effect |
|---|---|
| The Quraysh make treaties with neighboring tribes. | |
| | Mecca becomes the most successful trade center in Arabia. |

# CHAPTER 3
# Lesson 1 Summary
## Desert Bloom—Caravan Cities

(*Across the Centuries* pp. 52–57)

**Thinking Focus:** What different ways of life did people have in the Arabian Peninsula in A.D. 500?

## Early Arabia

The people who lived in the Arabian Peninsula around A.D. 500 adapted their lives to the geography of the region. The peninsula has fertile areas that run along the coastal hills and mountains as well as desert regions that are dry most of the year. A place called the Empty Quarter in the center of the peninsula is one of the driest spots on Earth.

People traveling in the desert depended on the water from wells at the **oases.** In A.D. 500, the oases of the Arabian Peninsula attracted **nomads** and their camel herds. The nomads moved from place to place following water and grazing land for their herds. When they visited the towns that formed around oases, they traded camel meat and milk for grain, weapons, cloth, and other goods. Some nomads settled near oases and farmed crops such as wheat and barley.

The nomadic families of Arabia belonged to a group of people who called themselves Arabs after the language they spoke. Nomads lived together in extended family groups. These families often joined together to form **tribes.** A respected elder settled conflicts within the tribe.

Some Arabs called *hanif* believed in one God. The Arab nomads believed in a Creator, as well as lesser gods and spirits.

Because water and grazing land were scarce, tribes sometimes fought over water rights. Larger tribes might charge money to smaller tribes for the use of an oasis.

**?** Describe the lifestyle of the Arab nomads.

**oasis**
(ō-ā´sĭs)
a small area in the desert that has water from springs and wells (plural is oases)

**nomad**
(nō´măd´)
a member of a group that moves from place to place to find food, water, and grazing land for its herds

**tribe**
(trīb)
a social system made up of families with the same ancestors, language, and culture

*Summary continues
on next page*

## Towns and Trade

Between A.D. 500 and 600, the Arabian Peninsula was home to three groups: city dwellers, farming villagers, and nomadic tribes. These three groups worked well together. Towns were built along trade routes. Merchants and traders lived there, as well as craftspeople, scholars, and judges.

Seaports linked Arabia with Africa and Asia. Ivory and gold came from Africa. Spices and cloth came from India. The Arabs traded Arabian horses and camels. Wealthy Arab merchants who lived in the towns became leaders among the Arabs in the region. As people met the traders who moved between cities, they heard of places both near and far.

[?] Describe the lifestyle of the Arab town-dwellers.

## The Holy City of Mecca

Mecca formed where the main north-south and east-west trade routes crossed. Travelers stopped in Mecca to get water from its freshwater well. But according to Islamic teachings, the biblical Abraham was told by God to build the Ka'bah in Mecca as a house of worship. The Ka'bah is a cube-shaped, stone structure. It was a reminder of Abraham's belief in one God. Over time, people placed **idols** in it. It became a tradition to go on a **pilgrimage** to walk around the Ka'bah.

The Quraysh tribe became the keepers of the Ka'bah. They made treaties to prevent fighting and allow safe travel during pilgrimage season. These treaties made Mecca a safe place.

[?] How was Mecca different from other Arab trading cities?

**idol**
(īd′l)

an image used as an object of worship

**pilgrimage**
(pĭl′grə-mĭj)

a trip to a holy place

### Trade in Arabia

| From India | From Africa | From Arabia |
|---|---|---|
| cloth | ivory | horses |
| spices | gold | camels |

**CHAPTER 3**

# Lesson 2 Preview
## Muhammad and Islam

(*Across the Centuries* pp. 58–64)

### Development of Islam

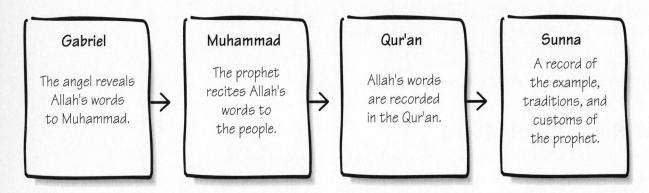

1. **Look at the graphic organizer above. Then read the following sentences and fill in the blanks.**

   a. Whose words are recorded in the Qur'an?

   _____

   b. Whose actions are discussed in the Sunna?

   _____

2. **Look at the drawing on page 61 and read the caption. What do you think might be another word for minaret?**

   _____

CHAPTER 3

# Lesson 2 Reading Strategy
## Muhammad and Islam

(*Across the Centuries* pp. 58–64)

**Self-Question** This reading strategy helps you stay focused on what you read. Ask yourself questions before you read a section. Then read to see if you can find the answer to your questions.

1. Read the heading "The Life of the Prophet" on page 59. Which question below do you expect to have answered in the paragraphs that follow this heading? Circle the letter next to the best question.
   a. What did Muhammad do before he became a prophet?
   b. What trade routes ran through the area where Muhammad lived?
   c. What were Jewish temples called during Muhammad's time?

2. Now read the section "Life of the Prophet" on pages 59–61 to see if the question you chose was answered. If it was, write the answer to the question.

   _____

   _____

3. Read the heading "The Teachings of Islam" on page 61. Write down a question you expect will be answered by the section.

   _____

   Now read the section "The Teachings of Islam" on pages 61–63 to see if the question you wrote down was answered. If it was, write the answer to your question.

   _____

   _____

   _____

   _____

# Lesson 2 Summary
## Muhammad and Islam

*(Across the Centuries pp. 58–64)*

---

**Thinking Focus:** Find details to support the statement, "Islam, like other religions, is not only a system of beliefs but also a way of life."

---

## The Life of the Prophet

In about A.D. 570, Muhammad was born into the Quraysh tribe. **Muslims** believe that on a visit to Mount Hira in 610, the angel Gabriel spoke to him. The angel told him to speak to others in the name of God. Muslims say this was the first of Muhammad's many messages from God. The messages made Muhammad sure that there was one God. Belief in one God is called **monotheism**. Allah, the God Muhammad believed in, is the same God as that of Judaism and Christianity. Muhammad called his faith **Islam**. Believers in Islam are called Muslims.

Muhammad began to preach to members of his tribe. Quraysh leaders in Mecca became worried. They refused to trade with Muhammad and his followers. When Arabs outside of Mecca became interested in Muhammad's message, the Quraysh leaders planned to kill the prophet. In 622, Muhammad and his followers left Mecca for Medina. This migration was known as the Hijra.

Over the next eight years Islam grew. Muhammad's enemies tried to get rid of Islam. But nomadic tribes and some Meccan leaders joined the Muslims. Muhammad created an army of 10,000 men, which, in 630, marched into Mecca. The city gave up without a fight. Muhammad removed the idols from the Ka'bah, which again became a place of worship for the one God. The area around the Ka'bah became the first **mosque**. When Muhammad died in 632, many people in the central and western coastal regions of Arabia were Muslims.

**?** How was the religion of Islam founded, and how did it spread?

**Muslim**
(mŭz´ləm)
a believer in Islam

**monotheism**
(mŏn´ə-thē-ĭz´əm)
belief in only one God

**Islam**
(ĭs-läm´)
a religion based on the teachings of the prophet Muhammad

**mosque**
(mŏsk)
a Muslim church or house of worship

*Summary continues on next page*

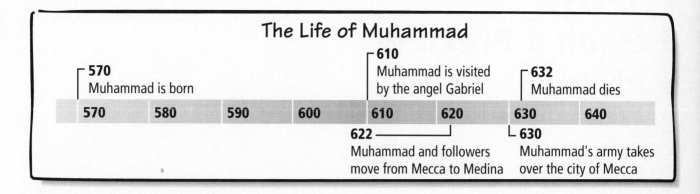

The Life of Muhammad

**570**
Muhammad is born

**610**
Muhammad is visited
by the angel Gabriel

**632**
Muhammad dies

| 570 | 580 | 590 | 600 | 610 | 620 | 630 | 640 |

**622**
Muhammad and followers
move from Mecca to Medina

**630**
Muhammad's army takes
over the city of Mecca

## The Teachings of Islam

Muhammad's followers wrote down all of Allah's messages and put
them into one book called the **Qur'an**. Many of them also learned the
hadith, or words and actions of Muhammad. Collections of hadith are
called the **Sunna**.

 The Five Pillars of Islam guide the Muslim way of life. First, Muslims
must pledge their faith to Allah. Second, they must pray five times a day.
Third, they must give charity. Fourth, they must not eat or drink while
there is daylight during the Muslim month of Ramadan. Fifth, Muslims
who can afford it must make a pilgrimage to Mecca at least once.
Together, the Qur'an and Sunna are the religious and social guidelines
for the Islamic way of life. Muslims also believe that the Jews' and
Christians' holy book, the Bible, is based on the word of God.

**?** Why are the Qur'an and Sunna important to Muslims?

**Qur'an**
(kə-răn´)

the book of Islam that is
believed to hold the
words Allah spoke to
Muhammad

**Sunna**
(sōōn´ə)

a collection of the words
and deeds of
Muhammad

## An Islamic Way of Life

The Qur'an and the Sunna present the moral laws that Muslims live
by. These laws cover religious life, as well as such things as diet,
marriage, and divorce. The laws also cover legal contracts, or
agreements. Unlike other societies of the time, women were given clear
rules for marriage. They were also given the right to an education. In
addition, women were able to control the money they made, to make
contracts, and to serve as witnesses in courts. Many of these laws and
rights are still in effect. However, the social customs in some countries
have overruled these laws.

**?** How does Islam affect many aspects of daily life for Muslims?

Name: _____                    Date: _____

# Lesson 3 Preview
## Early Islam

(*Across the Centuries* pp. 65–68)

## The Caliphate

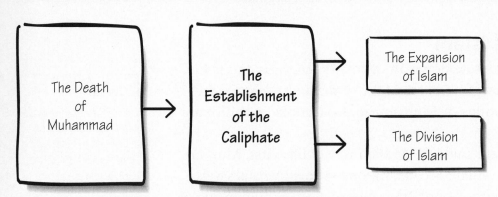

1. **Look at the graphic organizer above. Then read the following sentences and fill in the blanks.**

   a. According to the graphic, the Caliphate was established as a result of

      _____

      _____.

   b. According to the graphic, what happened to the Islamic faith once the Caliphate was established?

      _____

      _____

2. **Look at the map on page 67. Name the six bodies of water that touched parts of the Muslim empire.**

   _____

   _____

   _____

   _____

   _____

   _____

CHAPTER 3

# Lesson 3 Reading Strategy
## Early Islam

*(Across the Centuries* pp. 65–68)

**Summarize** This reading strategy helps you remember key points about what you have read. When you get to a good break in your reading, stop and write down the main ideas of what you have read.

1. **Read the section "The First Caliph" on page 66. What is the best summary of how the first caliph came to power? Circle the letter next to the best answer.**
   a. There were four men who wanted to become the caliph after Muhammad died.
   b. Abu Bakr was Muhammad's father-in-law and the two men were close friends.
   c. Abu Bakr was chosen as the new caliph by a group of tribal leaders.

2. **Now read the section "The Next Two Caliphs" on pages 66–67. Write a one-sentence summary about how the third caliph came to power.**

   _____

   _____

3. **Read the first three paragraphs of the section "Early Political Division" on page 67. Then summarize what happened after Uthman was murdered.**

   _____

   _____

   _____

   _____

# Lesson 3 Summary
## Early Islam

(*Across the Centuries* pp. 65–68)

**Thinking Focus:** What challenges did Muslims face after Muhammad's death?

## The First Caliph

When Muhammad died, his most trusted advisers met to decide who would be the **caliph**. They knew the caliph would not be a prophet, but a political and military leader. The man they chose for the job was Muhammad's father-in-law, Abu Bakr.

After Muhammad's death, some of the tribes in the area had tried to revolt and decided they were no longer Muslims. Abu Bakr stopped the revolt and convinced them the state was strong. He also united the Arabs and began to extend the Muslim state outside of Arabia. His armies moved north to Syria and Mesopotamia.

? How was the problem of Muhammad's successor resolved?

**caliph**
(kā′lĭf)

the leader of a Muslim state; means "one who comes after"

**council**
(koun′səl)

a group that met to choose the next caliph

## The Next Two Caliphs

Abu Bakr ruled for only two years. Before he died, he chose Umar as his successor. Umar and his armies conquered more lands. The Muslims were tolerant of the people they conquered. They let Jews and Christians keep their synagogues and churches. The Muslims promised these people safety. Some non-Muslim groups aided Muslim takeovers, since they thought the Muslims would be better rulers.

In 644, the dying Umar named a **council** to choose the next caliph. The council chose Uthman. Uthman continued to expand the empire. Muslim forces pushed into North Africa. By 661, they had conquered all of Persia.

? Why was the expansion of the Muslim empire so successful?

*Summary continues on next page*

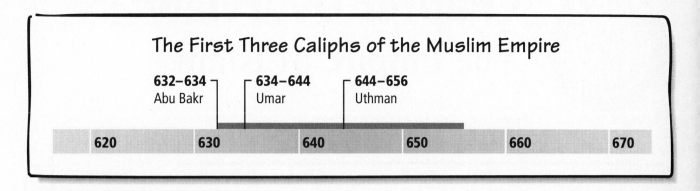

## Early Political Division

The Muslim Empire expanded quickly, but not without problems. Uthman made many enemies when he chose members of his own family to lead some parts of the empire. In 656, a group of angry Muslims killed Uthman.

Ali was the natural choice for the next caliph. He had been Muhammad's cousin and son-in-law. But a relative of Uthman, Muawiya, had a following in Syria. He said Ali had no right to rule. Before the two sides came to battle, they agreed to negotiate, but talks failed to solve the conflict. Ali ruled for only two years before he was killed by an angry supporter. In 661, Muawiya became caliph.

Ali's followers became known as **Shiites**. They accepted only members of Muhammad's family as caliphs. They did not accept the first three caliphs, who had not been blood relatives of Muhammad. Those Muslims who claim to follow the Sunna are called **Sunni** Muslims. They believed in the election of the first four caliphs, called the Rightly Guided Caliphs. Both the Sunni and the Shiite Muslims still exist. Sunni Muslims make up about 80 percent of the Muslims in the world today. The two groups have many differences. But both believe in Allah and the prophet Muhammad. And both believe that the Qur'an is the word of Allah.

**[?]** How did the division of Muslims into Sunnis and Shiites come about?

**Shiite**
(shē´ĭt´)
a member of the branch of Islam that supports only the blood relatives of Muhammad as caliphs

**Sunni**
(sōon´ē)
the branch of Islam that supports the first four caliphs as successors to Muhammad

# Chapter Overview
## The Empire of Islam

**Fill in the blanks below with information from the chapter.**

**When:**
635–1492
**Where:**
Arabia and parts of Africa, Southwest Asia, Spain
**Who:**
Muslims

## Muslim Achievements

### The Umayyads

Expanded to: _____

Achievements: _____

_____

Dates of Decline: _____

### The Abbasids

Expanded to: _____

Achievements: _____

_____

Dates of Decline: _____

### Muslim Spain

Expanded to: _____

Achievements: _____

_____

Dates of Decline: _____

CHAPTER 4

# Lesson 1 Preview
## A Century of Expansion

(*Across the Centuries* pp. 78–84)

### Development of the Muslim Empire

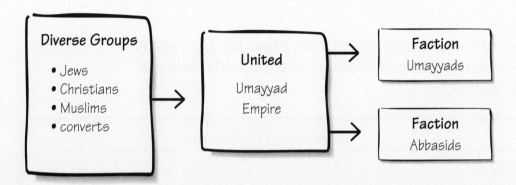

1. **Look at the graphic organizer above. Which diverse groups were included in the Umayyad Empire?**

_____

_____

_____

2. **Look at the map on pages 80–81. Then answer the following questions:**

   **a.** What rivers flow into the Persian Gulf?

   _____

   _____

   _____

   **b.** Alexandria is near what body of water?

   _____

**CHAPTER 4**

# Lesson 1 Reading Strategy
## A Century of Expansion

(*Across the Centuries* pp. 78–84)

**Compare and Contrast** This reading strategy helps you understand how events are similar and different. As you read about historical events, think about how they compare and contrast with events you already know.

1. Read the section "Treatment of Non-Muslims" on pages 80–82. Then fill in the chart below with information comparing Muslims with Christians and Jews in the Muslim Empire.

| Muslims | Jews and Christians |
|---------|---------------------|
|         |                     |
|         |                     |

2. Use the information from your chart to write down one way the Muslims were like the Jews and Christians and one way they were different.

   _____

   _____

3. Read the first two paragraphs of the section "Umayyad Unity" on page 83. Write two sentences that compare and contrast the Muslim Empire before and after the rule of Abd al Malik.

   _____

   _____

   _____

   _____

# Lesson 1 Summary
## A Century of Expansion

(*Across the Centuries* pp. 78–84)

Summary also on
Audiotape

---

**Thinking Focus:** How did the Umayyads unite the many lands and peoples of the Muslim Empire?

---

## Expansion Under Umayyad Rule

In A.D. 635, Muslim soldiers from Arabia attacked Byzantine forces in Damascus, Syria. The people of Damascus helped the Muslim Arabs. They believed the Muslims would be better rulers than the Byzantines.

The Muslim soldiers who fought at Damascus helped build an **empire**. They fought to bring Islam to the people of the Middle East. After they took over Syria, they went on to take Mesopotamia in 637. They conquered Persia by the mid-600s.

One of the soldiers who had helped capture Damascus in 635 was Muawiya. He was the leader of the Umayyads. He built a huge army. In 661, he took control of the Muslim Empire. He moved the capital from Medina to Damascus. Members of Muawiya's family, the Umayyads, would rule for 90 years. The Umayyads were good military leaders. The Muslim Empire grew during their years of power.

The Umayyad armies moved west into North Africa. Soon the Berbers who lived along the northern coast of the Sahara converted to Islam. In 711, the Berbers helped the Muslims conquer Spain. From Spain, they raided France. But in 732, the Muslims met with Charles Martel and his army of Franks. Martel's forces stopped the Muslims at the Battle of Tours. The battle meant that Europe would be Christian and not Muslim.

❓ What changes did the Umayyads bring to the Muslim Empire?

**empire**
(ĕm´pīr´)
number of peoples or provinces under one ruler

*Summary continues on next page*

---

# An Empire of Many Peoples

The Muslim Empire included Jews, Christians, and people who believed in many gods. Many of these people converted to Islam. The Umayyads let Jews and Christians have religious freedom. They did not have to serve in the army. Instead they paid a tax. Non-Muslims often held key government positions. The caliph Muawiya ruled over the empire with a **bureaucracy**. He appointed **emirs** to rule the provinces. Some emirs ruled strictly in order to wipe out **dissent** among the people, while others were fair and just.

**?** How did Muslims treat people of different beliefs?

# Umayyad Unity

Abd al Malik made Arabic the official language of the Muslim Empire. People spoke their own languages, but government business had to be in Arabic. He also set up a money system so that everyone in the empire used the same kind of money.

After the Muslims conquered new lands, the first thing they did was build mosques. The mosques were built of local materials.

**?** How did Abd al Malik unify the Umayyad Empire?

# The Umayyad Downfall

By 750, the Muslim Empire had stopped growing. Many non-Muslims had converted to Islam and paid fewer taxes. The empire had less money. Some people thought that the Umayyad leaders were not religious enough. Groups like the Abbasids worked to end Umayyad rule. Some stories tell how Abdullah, an Abbasid general, invited Umayyad leaders to a feast and killed all but one of them. That one, Abd al Rahman, escaped to Spain, where he began a new government. The Muslim Empire in the east was now run by the Abbasids. The Umayyads controlled Spain.

**?** What political problems led to the downfall of the Umayyad Empire?

---

**bureaucracy**
(byōō-rŏk′rə-sē)

a power structure in which there is one person in charge at the top and many people at the bottom; workers at each level supervise those below them

**emir**
(ĭ-mîr′)

a government official in the Middle East appointed by the caliph

**dissent**
(dĭ-sĕnt′)

disagreement, especially with accepted religious practices

CHAPTER 4

# Lesson 2 Preview
## The Golden Age
(*Across the Centuries* pp. 85–92)

### The Abbasid Empire

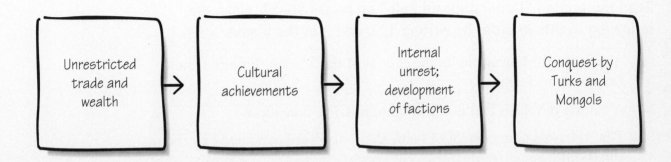

Unrestricted trade and wealth → Cultural achievements → Internal unrest; development of factions → Conquest by Turks and Mongols

1. **Look at the graphic organizer above. Then read the following sentences and fill in the blanks.**

   a. What allowed the cultural achievements of the Abbasid Empire?

   _____

   _____

   b. What things led to the conquest of the Abbasid Empire by the Turks and Mongols?

   _____

   _____

2. **Look at the map on page 85. Why do you think Baghdad was a good place for the capital of the Abbasid Empire?**

   _____

   _____

   _____

   _____

   _____

CHAPTER 4
# Lesson 2 Reading Strategy
## The Golden Age

(*Across the Centuries* pp. 85–92)

**Sequence** This reading strategy helps you follow the order of events. As you read, pay attention to dates and times, as well as to words such as *before*, *finally*, *after*, and *then*.

1. **Read the section "Under Abbasid Rule" on pages 86–87. Place the following events in order by writing 1, 2, and 3 in the blanks.**

—— Abu Jafar al Mansur moves the capital of the Muslim Empire from Damascus to Baghdad.

—— A culture develops that is Muslim but open to new ideas.

—— The Abbasids take control of lands that once were conquered by the Umayyads.

2. **Read the first paragraph in the section "Abbasid Culture" on page 88. What phrase helps you understand the sequence of events?**

_____

3. **Read the section "Bookmaking and Literature" on page 89. Place the following events in order by writing 1, 2 and 3 in the blanks.**

—— Chinese papermakers teach the Abbasids how to make paper.

—— Abbasids capture Chinese papermakers.

—— Caliph al Ma'mun founds the House of Wisdom.

4. **Read the section "A Divided Empire" on page 92. Fill in the blanks below with the correct dates and events.**

| _____ | 969 | _____ | 1258 |
|---|---|---|---|
| Abbasids take over Umayyad Empire | The Fatimids conquer most of _____ | Baghdad is conquered by Seljuk Turks | Baghdad is destroyed by _____ |

# Lesson 2 Summary
## The Golden Age

(*Across the Centuries* pp. 85–92)

**Thinking Focus:** How did the same wealth that brought the Abbasids to power lead to their downfall?

## Under Abbasid Rule

The Abbasid Empire lasted from 750 to 1258. In 752, caliph Abu Jafar al Mansur moved the capital of the Muslim Empire from Damascus, Syria, to a new city he built, Baghdad, in Mesopotamia. There the Abbasid family had much support. The Abbasid government had a strong army, too. It also had spies who told the caliph about any conflict in the empire. The Muslim Empire took in many different cultures, especially that of Persia. Those cultures blended with the Arab way of life to produce a new Muslim culture.

**?** How did the Abbasids get and keep control of their empire?

## The New Capital of Baghdad

The city of Baghdad had a strong economy based on taxes, manufacturing, and trade. The city was also known for its science and technology. The Abbasids increased food production by bringing water to dry areas through underground canals. Traders came from as far away as Africa, Europe, and Southeast Asia. They bought leather, cloth, paper, metal, and perfumes from the merchants in Baghdad. The Abbasids also developed a system of banking that was used throughout the empire. People could buy things on credit. Trade with many different countries brought great wealth to the Abbasids.

**?** Why did Baghdad become such an important center of world trade?

*Summary continues on next page*

# Abbasid Culture

From 800 to 1000, the Abbasids created great art and literature. In 751, they captured some Chinese papermakers and learned how to make paper and books. With more books, people became more interested in learning. Jewish, Muslim, and Christian scholars worked to translate Greek, African, and Asian classics into Arabic. The Abbasids also became famous for their poetry and their **calligraphy.** The walls of mosques were covered with beautiful writing. Muslims were not allowed to create idols, or pictures of people or animals, so they drew patterns.

**[?]**  What achievements in culture led to this period being known as the Golden Age?

**calligraphy**
(kə-lĭg´rə-fē)
the art of fine handwriting

**faction**
(făk´shən)
a group of people who form a minority in disagreement with a larger group

# Abbasid Achievements in Learning

Muslim scholars were very advanced. Astronomers mapped the solar system and believed that the Earth was round, not flat. Great mathematicians produced work we still use today. Abbasid doctors performed surgery in clean hospitals that were free to the public. Avicenna was a famous doctor who wrote a book called *The Canon of Medicine*. It had all medical knowledge of the time and described ways to treat diseases.

**[?]**  How was Abbasid Baghdad famous as a center of scientific, mathematical, and medical achievements?

# A Divided Empire

By 1000, the Abbasids had lost some important trade routes. This hurt their economy. They raised taxes in order to keep their expensive lifestyle. **Factions** formed against the Abbasids, and some left the empire. Others took over far away provinces. The Fatimids broke away from the Abbasids and by 969, had control of most of North Africa.

Seljuk Turks from central Asia conquered Baghdad in 1055. The caliph remained but was powerless. In 1258, Mongol invaders took Baghdad, destroyed the city, and ended the Abbasid Empire.

**[?]**  What led to the division of the Abbasid Empire?

CHAPTER 4

# Lesson 3 Preview
## Islamic Spain

(*Across the Centuries* pp. 95–100)

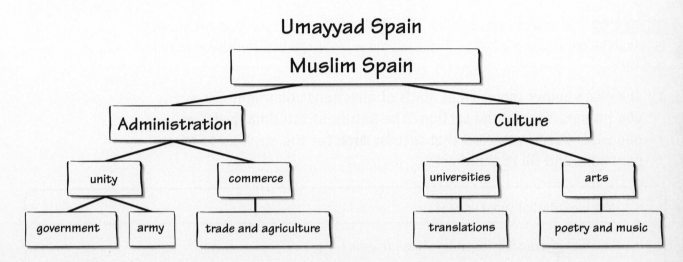

Umayyad Spain

Muslim Spain

Administration — Culture

unity — commerce — universities — arts

government — army — trade and agriculture — translations — poetry and music

1. **Look at the graphic organizer above. Then read the following sentences and fill in the blanks.**

   a. What income contributed to the administration of Muslim Spain?

   _____

   _____

   b. Why were the universities of Muslim Spain important?

   _____

   _____

2. **Look at the graph on page 98 and fill in the blanks below.**

   Around the year 1000, Rome had fewer than _____ people.

   Baghdad had _____ people.

CHAPTER 4
# Lesson 3 Reading Strategy
## Islamic Spain

(*Across the Centuries* pp. 95–100)

**Self-Question** This reading strategy helps you stay focused on what you read. Ask yourself questions before you read a section. Then read to see if you can find the answer to your questions.

1.  The chart below shows what kinds of questions you might ask as you prepare to read the section "The Return of the Umayyads" on pages 95–96. As you read that section, look for the answers to these questions and fill in the chart.

| | |
|---|---|
| a.  How was Muslim Spain united? | |
| b.  Who was responsible for uniting Muslim Spain? | |
| c.  What were the results of unification? | |

2.  Read the heading "Glory of Cordoba" and the first paragraph that follows on page 96. Which question below would you expect to have answered by reading the section? Circle the letter next to the best question.
    a.  What were some of the subjects studied by scholars who visited Cordoba?
    b.  What military tactics did Abd al Rahman III use?
    c.  Do many Americans visit Cordoba today?

3.  Read the section "Glory of Cordoba" on pages 96–99 to see if the question you chose was answered. If it was, write the answer to the question.

    _____

    _____

    _____

    _____

# Lesson 3 Summary
## Islamic Spain

*(Across the Centuries* pp. 95–100)

---

**Thinking Focus:** How did Muslim culture influence Spain?

## The Return of the Umayyads

Abd al Rahman was an Umayyad leader. He escaped to Spain in 750, when the Abbasids took control of the Muslim Empire. When he got there, he saw that Spain did not have one Muslim government over the whole country. But there were some Umayyad forces. They made Abd al Rahman their leader. He set up an independent Muslim kingdom and eventually took over all of Muslim Spain. He chose the ancient Roman city of Cordoba as his capital. His kingdom became so strong that it until 1000 it was rarely invaded.

About 200 years later, during the 49-year rule of Abd al Rahman III, from 912 to 961, Muslim Spain reached its high point. Abd al Rahman III called himself caliph and copied the government of the Abbasids in Baghdad. His huge army protected the kingdom from rival Muslims in the south and Christians in the north.

**?** How did the Umayyads unify and protect Spain?

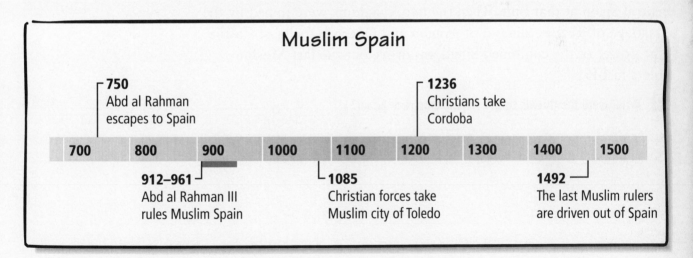

**Muslim Spain**

| 750 Abd al Rahman escapes to Spain | | | | | 1236 Christians take Cordoba | | | |
|---|---|---|---|---|---|---|---|---|
| 700 | 800 | 900 | 1000 | 1100 | 1200 | 1300 | 1400 | 1500 |
| | 912–961 Abd al Rahman III rules Muslim Spain | | 1085 Christian forces take Muslim city of Toledo | | | 1492 The last Muslim rulers are driven out of Spain | | |

*Summary continues on next page*

# Glory of Cordoba

Abd al Rahman III made Cordoba a great city. It was large and well run. It had 3,000 mosques. The largest of these was called the Great Mosque. The city also had thousands of palaces. In 1000, it was western Europe's biggest city, with 450,000 people.

The arts were well supported in Cordoba. There were 70 libraries. The largest had 500,000 books. There was a university and a law school. Scholars came from all over to study in Spain. They brought learning into Cordoba and took new ideas with them when they left. This love of learning was Cordoba's **legacy** to future cultures.

Cordoba was a center of learning for both Muslims and non-Muslims. For many years, it was the center of Sephardic culture, the culture of Jewish Spain. Jewish scholars, poets, and scientists thrived until 1492, when the Christians drove them out.

Merchants were another part of Cordoba's success. They sold leather, carpets, paper, and many other things. Cordoba became known as a place of skilled workers and good products.

**?** What were the greatest achievements of Cordoba?

**legacy**
(lĕg´ə-sē)
something handed down from the past

# The Loss of Spain

By the 1000s, Christian forces from the north of Spain began to move south. Christians call this period the Reconquest. In 1085, Christian forces took the Muslim city of Toledo. The rest of Muslim Spain slowly fell to the Christians. Cordoba was conquered in 1236. Two powerful Catholic kingdoms, Aragon and Castile, ruled northern and central Spain at that time. Then the two kingdoms were joined by the marriage of King Ferdinand of Aragon and Queen Isabella of Castile. The power of the combined kingdoms drove out the last Muslim rulers in 1492.

**?** What were the threats to the Islamic Empire in Spain?

# Chapter Overview
## West Africa

Fill in the blank spaces below with information from the chapter.

### West African Empires

**When:**
500 B.C.– A.D. 1590

**Where:**
West Africa

---

### Origins of the Empires

**Who:** The Nok People

**When:** _____

---

### Ghana

**Traded Goods:**
- _____
- _____

**Crops raised:**
- sorghum
- rice
- yams

### Mali

**A Famous Leader:**
- _____

**Religions practiced:**
- Islam
- Traditional gods

### Songhai

**Size of empire:**
_____
_____

**Dates of empire:**
_____
_____
_____

---

### Village Society in West Africa

**Crops:** millet, sorghum, _____

**Understanding kinship:** Rights and Responsibilities

CHAPTER 5
# Lesson 1 Preview
## The Roots of Mighty Empires
(*Across the Centuries* pp. 108–111)

### Ancient West Africa

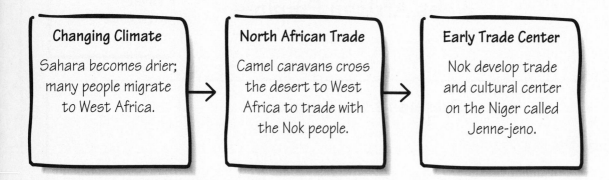

| Changing Climate | North African Trade | Early Trade Center |
|---|---|---|
| Sahara becomes drier; many people migrate to West Africa. | Camel caravans cross the desert to West Africa to trade with the Nok people. | Nok develop trade and cultural center on the Niger called Jenne-jeno. |

1. **Look at the graphic organizer above. Then read and answer the following questions:**

   a. What happened as the result of the Sahara becoming drier?

   _____

   _____

   _____

   _____

   b. What animals were used in caravans traveling across the desert?

   _____

   _____

   c. What is the name of the trade and cultural center on the Niger River?

   _____

2. **Look at the map on page 109 in your text. What is the approximate distance in miles between Jenne-jeno and Nok?**

   _____

# Lesson 1 Reading Strategy
## The Roots of Mighty Empires

(*Across the Centuries* pp. 108–111)

**Cause and Effect** This reading strategy helps you understand events and why they occur. As you read, think about the factors that caused an event. Then think about what the effects of that event may be.

1. **Read the section "A Land of Many Climates" on pages 108–110. What caused many Africans to move to West Africa?**
   a. Ghanaian soldiers
   b. changes in temperature and amount of rainfall
   c. new oases

2. **Read the section "A New Technology" on page 110. What was one important effect of trade between West Africa and North Africa?**

   _____

   _____

3. **Read the section "An Ancient Trade Center" on pages 110–111. What was the effect of the Niger River's annual flooding?**

   _____

   _____

4. **Fill in the chart below.**

| Cause | Effect |
|-------|--------|
| The Niger floods Jenne-jeno. | |
| The people of Jenne-jeno have surplus crops. | |
| | Jenne-jeno grows into a large trade center. |

# Lesson 1 Summary
## The Roots of Mighty Empires

*(Across the Centuries* pp. 108–111)

**Thinking Focus:** What are some of the ways the early West Africans developed prosperous cities in a landscape with such a varying climate?

## A Land of Many Climates

Thousands of years ago, a change of climate in the Sahara forced people to move. Some people went to West Africa and lived in the **savanna** on the southern border of the Sahara. This savanna is known as the **sahel**. Other people settled in the savannas and rain forests of a more fertile area along the Niger River.

**?** Describe the climate and terrain in each of West Africa's major land regions.

**savanna**
(sə-văn´ə)

an area of grasslands with scattered trees and plant growth

**sahel**
(sə-hāl´)

a strip of dry grasslands on the southern Sahara border; also known as "the shore of the desert"

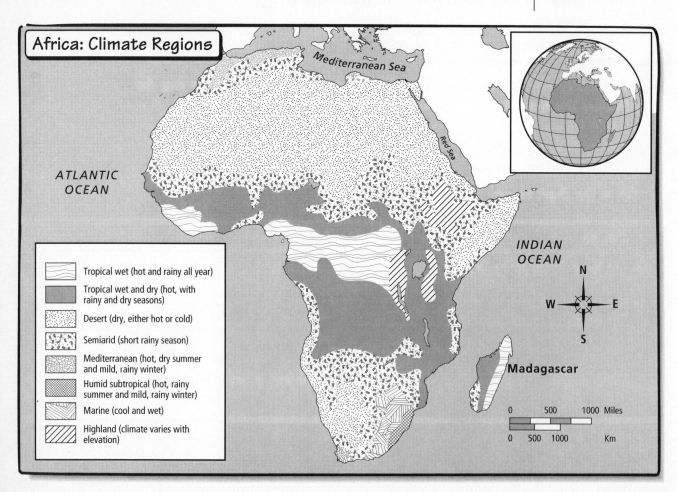

**Africa: Climate Regions**

Mediterranean Sea

Red Sea

ATLANTIC OCEAN

INDIAN OCEAN

Madagascar

N W E S

Tropical wet (hot and rainy all year)

Tropical wet and dry (hot, with rainy and dry seasons)

Desert (dry, either hot or cold)

Semiarid (short rainy season)

Mediterranean (hot, dry summer and mild, rainy winter)

Humid subtropical (hot, rainy summer and mild, rainy winter)

Marine (cool and wet)

Highland (climate varies with elevation)

0      500      1000 Miles

0    500   1000          Km

## A New Technology

Travel across the Sahara was difficult, but West Africans still traded with North Africans. Camel caravans traveled across the desert, and people exchanged goods and ideas. For example, the Nok people of West Africa learned how to make iron from North Africans. The Nok lived between 500 B.C. and A.D. 200 in what is now the country of Nigeria. They began making iron spear points and farming tools as early as 450 B.C.

The Nok were skilled potters, too. They used clay to build their huts and make sculptures. The Nok shared their knowledge of iron making and pottery with the people they met in trade.

? What aspect of Nok culture demonstrates that trade had a major impact on Nok life?

## An Ancient Trade Center

In 1977, scientists found the remains of an ancient city, called Jenne-jeno. Jenne-jeno lies about two miles from the modern city of Jenne in the Republic of Mali. The remains found at Jenne-jeno include iron and clay artifacts like those made by the Nok people.

Jenne-jeno was built on a flood plain on an inland **delta** of the Niger River. The Niger flooded the area every year, leaving rich, moist land on which to grow rice and raise cattle. The people also caught fish in the Niger. Trade along the Niger linked Jenne-jeno with cities to the north and south. Camel caravans linked it with North Africa. From the north, traders brought back salt, copper, and stone. From the south, they brought gold. Some people in the city became skilled in crafts. Archaeologists have discovered iron tools, copper and gold jewelry, and clay animals among the remains.

Life in Jenne-jeno flourished from 250 B.C. to A.D. 1400. Then the city was abandoned. Since the nearby city of Jenne was founded about the same time, it is possible the people of Jenne-jeno moved to Jenne.

? How did the people of Jenne-jeno obtain the resources they could not produce?

**delta**
(dĕl′tə)

a triangular-shaped land area made of mud and silt deposited at a river's mouth

CHAPTER 5

# Lesson 2 Preview
## The Empire of Ghana

(*Across the Centuries* pp. 112–117)

### The Trading Empire of Ghana

1. **Look at the graphic organizer above. Then fill in the blanks using the words below.**

   | Ghana | monarchy | North Africans | trade |
   |-------|----------|----------------|-------|

   a. Its location helped Ghana prosper as a center of _____.

   b. Desert tribes and _____ overthrew the king of

   _____.

2. **Look at the picture on page 113. It shows blocks of salt used for trade. Find at least one other picture in this lesson that shows something people traded in Ghana. Write the page number(s) and describe items traded at the markets in Ghana.**

   _____

   _____

   _____

   _____

   _____

   _____

   _____

Reading Support Resources

CHAPTER 5
# Lesson 2 Reading Strategy
## The Empire of Ghana

*(Across the Centuries* pp. 112–117)

**Predict/Infer** This reading strategy helps you understand what you have read and what you will read next. Before you read a section, think about the titles, pictures, and captions. Then think about what will happen in the selection.

1. Read the heading "A Center of Trade" on page 113. Look at the picture and read the caption. What do you predict will happen to trade in Ghana?

   a. Trade routes will pass Ghana by.
   b. Ghana will become prosperous from trading valuable goods.
   c. Salt will lose its value, and trade will collapse.

2. **Name two clues from the heading and the caption that helped you make your prediction.**

   _____

   _____

3. **Read the section "A Diverse Capital" and the next heading on page 115. What do you predict will happen to the Muslims in Koumbi?**

   a. They will influence the Ghanaians.
   b. They will be kicked out of Ghana.
   c. They will become architects.

   **How did your knowledge of Koumbi's diversity help you make your prediction?**

   _____

   _____

4. **Read the section "A New Religion" on pages 115 and 116. Then fill in the chart below.**

   | What I Know | What I Predict |
   |-------------|----------------|
   |             |                |
   |             |                |
   |             |                |
   |             |                |

# Lesson 2 Summary
## The Empire of Ghana

*(Across the Centuries pp. 112–117)*

**Thinking Focus:** What effect did trade have on the people of Ghana?

## A Center of Trade

Ghana was the ancient kingdom of the Soninke people. It lay between the Sahel and the Sahara in the north, and the highlands and tropical rain forests in the south. By the late 900s, the Soninke ruled more than 100,000 square miles and hundreds of thousands of people. They made Ghana the first great trading empire in West Africa.

Ghana was first an agricultural kingdom. People farmed, raised livestock, built cities, and created art and music. But Ghana's central location made it a good place for trade. Traders from the salt mines to the north and the gold fields to the south passed through Ghana. The Senegal and Gambia rivers aided in communication and the transport of goods. Salt was scarce in southern Ghana, but gold was not. West African gold became important to Europe, the Middle East, and North Africa, for use as money and jewelry. People traded salt and gold in equal amounts—a pound of gold for a pound of salt.

### Ghana: A Trading Crossroad

Salt from mines in the northern Sahara → Ghana becomes rich from gold and salt trade ← Gold from mines in southern Ghana

❓ What combination of geographic and economic factors made Ghana an ideal trade center?

*Summary continues on next page*

## A Diverse Capital

From about 800 to 1050, the gold and salt trade thrived in Ghana. Most of the traders in Ghana were Muslims. The Soninke kings had their own traditional religion. They were tolerant of Islam, but they wanted to keep it separate. So they divided Koumbi, and other trading towns, into two sections. These sections were linked by a boulevard, which is a wide street. The Muslim section of Koumbi had mosques, one-and two-story stone homes, and the market. The Soninke section was a walled city with wood or clay houses, straw roofs, and a large wood and stone palace for the king.

**?** How did the two sections of Koumbi differ from each other?

## A New Religion

In the 900s, many Arab merchants came to live in Ghana. They brought with them a system of writing and numbers and the Islamic religion. The Mandinke people from the southern Sahara were among the first converts to Islam. Because they were traders, they helped spread Muslim ideas in Africa.

Muslims practiced **patrilineal** succession, in which the throne passes from father to son. However, in Ghana, the king passed his right to the throne down to his sister's son, in **matrilineal** succession.

**?** In what ways did Ghanaians benefit from their contact with Arab traders?

## A Fallen Empire

The Almoravids were a Muslim political and spiritual movement to the north. As the Almoravids grew in power, wars spread and Ghana lost territory. When Ghana tried to regain its empire in 1087 it was too late. The empire had broken into separate kingdoms.

**?** How did the brief takeover by the Almoravids lead to Ghana's downfall?

**patrilineal**
(păt´rə-lĭn´ē-əl)

a system of passing power through the males of the family

**matrilineal**
(măt´rə-lĭn´ē-əl)

a system of passing power through the females of the family

*Summary continues on next page*

CHAPTER 5

# Lesson 3 Preview
## The Empires of Mali and Songhai

(*Across the Centuries* pp. 118–122)

## Mali and Songhai

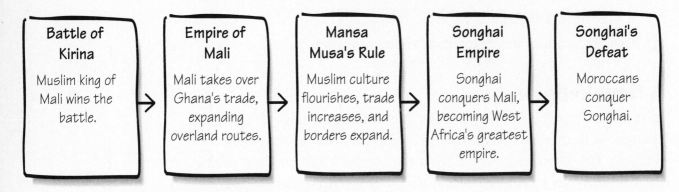

1.  **Look at the graphic organizer above. Place the events in order according to which happened first, second, third, fourth, and fifth.**

    ____ Muslim culture flourishes.

    ____ Mali takes over Ghana's trade.

    ____ Battle of Kirina

    ____ Songhai becomes West Africa's greatest empire.

    ____ Songhai is conquered.

2.  **Look at the maps on page 121. Then compare the extent of Ghana, Mali, and Songhai between 700 and 1600.**

    _____

    _____

    _____

    _____

    _____

    _____

    _____

    _____

CHAPTER 5

# Lesson 3 Reading Strategy
## The Empires of Mali and Songhai

(*Across the Centuries* pp. 118–122)

**Sequence** This reading strategy helps you follow the order of events. As you read, pay attention to dates and times, as well as to words such as *before*, *finally*, *after*, and *then*.

1. **Read the section "Mali Develops a Prosperous Trade" on pages 118 and 119. Place the following events in order by writing 1, 2, and 3 in the blanks.**

   —— Gold is discovered at Bure.

   —— Sundiata becomes king of Mali.

   —— Niani becomes a trade center.

2. **Read the first paragraph of the section "Mansa Musa Enriches the Empire" on page 119. Place the following events in order:**

   —— Musa became king.

   —— Conversions greatly increased.

3. **Read the first sentence of the section "Power Shifts to Songhai" on page 120. What word helps you understand the sequence of events?**

   _____

4. **Read from the heading "Songhai Collapses" on page 122 to the end of the lesson. Complete the time line below with events from the following list.**

   Moroccans lose interest.        Salt mines are captured.
                                   Pasha conquers most of Songhai.

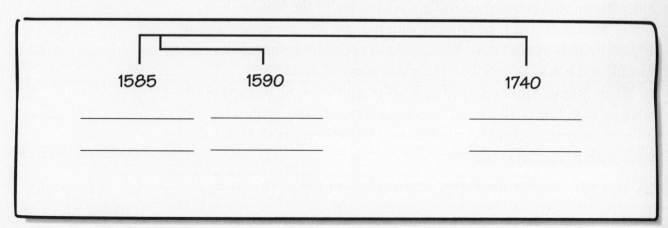

# Lesson 3 Summary
## The Empires of Mali and Songhai

(*Across the Centuries* pp. 118–122)

**Thinking Focus:** What events led to the development of the great trade empires of Mali and Songhai?

## Mali Develops a Prosperous Trade

Sundiata became king of the new empire in Mali. **Griots** still tell the tale of his victory. He made his capital at Niani, on the upper Niger River. Sundiata relied on his army to extend the borders of Mali. Then he focused on restoring wealth in his kingdom.

He restored the salt and gold trade, with Niani as the new trade center. Sundiata and his successors expanded trade routes. They went north and east to Egypt and Tunis. Mali controlled salt mines in the north, at Taghaza. It had copper mines in the east, at Takedda. It had gold mines in the south, at Wangara, and at Bure, near the capital. Thus the Niger River became a busy trade route. By the late 1300s, Mali was three times as large as Ghana had been. It was the most powerful kingdom in Africa.

**?** How did Sundiata and his armies extend Mali's trade empire?

> **griot**
> (grē´ō)
>
> a person who passes down customs, history, legend, art, and poetry through storytelling

## Mansa Musa Enriches the Empire

Mali's greatest ruler, Mansa Musa, came to the throne in 1307. Mansa Musa was a Muslim and he was tolerant of other beliefs. Like many other Muslims, Mansa Musa made a pilgrimage to the Muslim holy city of Mecca. In 1324, he brought with him 50,000 people and about 10,000 pounds of gold dust. Word of Mali's economic importance spread, and it was included on European maps of Africa.

When Mansa Musa returned to Mali from Mecca, he brought Arab scholars with him. Culture and learning grew in Niani, Timbuktu, and other trade centers. Trade expanded, too. Muslims came to Mali to trade with fellow believers.

**?** What effect did West African rulers' conversion to Islam have on the empire?

*Summary continues on next page*

## Power Shifts to Songhai

Mansa Musa died in 1332, and the kings who followed him could not hold Mali's vast lands. Under attack on all sides, Mali weakened. In 1464, under the leadership of a Songhai prince, Sunni Ali, the Songhai people began conquering their neighbors and expanding their kingdom. A new Songhai empire grew up out of Mali, as Mali had grown up out of Ghana.

In the 1490s, Askia Muhammad became king and declared Islam the state religion. Askia's armies expanded the borders of Songhai. Askia encouraged people to convert to Islam. He also invited Muslim scholars to his empire. Once again, the cities became centers of culture and learning. The number of Muslims—and Muslim traders—increased. In the late 1500s, the Songhai empire was larger and wealthier than Mali had ever been.

[?] How did Askia Muhammad's strong rule help Songhai become such a great trade empire?

## Songhai Collapses

Askia's heirs created a small but powerful Muslim group at the top of the ruling class. These people distanced themselves from non-Muslims. Some states resented the Muslim kings, and they broke away from the empire.

The biggest threat to the empire came from Morocco, in North Africa. In 1585, Morocco's ruler captured Songhai's salt mines in Taghaza. He also wanted control of Songhai's West African source of gold. In 1590, Morocco's ruler hired Muslim Spaniard Judar Pasha to conquer Songhai. Songhai had at least 25,000 soldiers who were armed with swords and arrows. Pasha's 1000 men had guns. They conquered Gao, then Timbuktu, and then most of Songhai.

[?] Why did the ruler of Morocco fight for control of Songhai?

CHAPTER 5

# Lesson 4 Preview
## Village Society in West Africa

(*Across the Centuries* pp. 124–127)

### West African Village Life

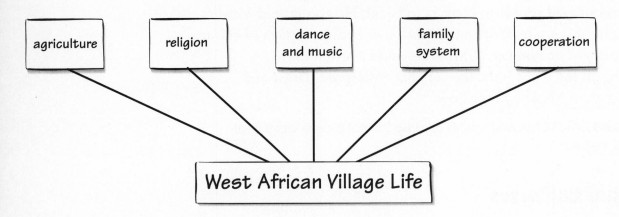

1. **Read the graphic organizer above. Then circle the correct answer to the following question:**

   Which of the following is <u>not</u> an important part of West African village life?

   **a.** religion
   **b.** trade
   **c.** family
   **d.** agriculture

2. **Look at the picture and read its caption on page 124 in your text. What are the people doing that is an important part of West African village life?**

   _____

   _____

   _____

   _____

   _____

   _____

Name: _____ Date: _____

CHAPTER 5

# Lesson 4 Reading Strategy
## Village Society in West Africa

(*Across the Centuries* pp. 124–127)

**Summarize** This reading strategy helps you remember key points about what you have read. When you get to a good break in your reading, stop and write down the main ideas of what you have read.

1. Read the section "Farming: A Way of Life" on pages 124 and 125. Then indicate which of the following is the best summary of the section by circling the letter next to your choice.

   a. Most West Africans lived in villages rather than cities. People in the villages traded goods.

   b. West African village life centered on farming. Farmers developed different methods to farm different land.

   c. Many people in West Africa were farmers. People of the rain forests could not raise cattle.

2. Read the section "Religion, Dance, and Music" on pages 125 and 126. Then write a short summary of the section.

   _____

   _____

3. Read the section "Village Life" on page 127. Then summarize the customs surrounding West African slavery.

   _____

   _____

4. Fill in the chart below to summarize important elements of village life in West Africa.

   <u>What I Learned</u>

   _____

   _____

   _____

   _____

# Lesson 4 Summary
## Village Society in West Africa

*(Across the Centuries* pp. 124–127)

**Thinking Focus:** How did the people in the rural villages of West Africa survive in their often unpredictable environment?

## Farming: A Way of Life

Early West Africans lived in small villages on riverbanks, on the savanna, or in the rain forests. Everyone in a village raised food, even iron makers and blacksmiths. They traded surplus crops for food they couldn't grow.

In the dry regions of the sahel, farmers grew millet and sorghum. In the wetter regions south of the sahel, people grew rice. In the dense West African rain forests, farmers made small clearings and grew edible roots.

West African farmers developed different farming methods to suit different kinds of land. For example, the Dogon people lived on cliffs south of the Niger River. Pools of rainwater formed in crevices between the rocks. So farmers brought fertile soil from the valley up the cliffs and made the pools into gardens.

### Climate and Crops

| Sahel Dry Regions | Wet Delta Region | Rain Forests |
|---|---|---|
| millet, sorghum | rice | edible roots |

**?** In what ways did the farming methods of rural peoples differ between regions?

*Summary continues
on next page*

Reading Support Resources

## Religion, Dance, and Music

Life in the villages of West Africa was often unpredictable. A drought, a flood, or an outbreak of disease could mean disaster. People hoped to avoid disaster by pleasing their gods.

West Africans believed in both a world on Earth and a spirit world. Their religion was meant to bring the two worlds together. Villagers appointed priests and **diviners** to communicate with the spirit world. They were also the villagers' source of healing. Diviners knew how to use herbs for healing and how to please their gods through rituals and dancing.

Villagers practiced **ancestor worship**, too. They respected their elders and prayed to their ancestors to influence the gods in their favor. Villagers also tried to contact and please spirits through music and dancing.

[?]  In what ways were the various religions of West African peoples similar?

## Village Life

People who lived in rural villages were members of large related families, or clans. Clan government was based on **kinship**. The male head of each clan was a chief and often a religious leader. Sometimes, a council of elders made up the village government. Yet everyone in the clan had a role to play. People did what was best for the clan.

If the clan owed money to another clan, a member might work as a temporary slave to help pay the debt. Permanent slaves became members of their owners' clans, and their children or grandchildren were usually born free.

[?]  Why was kinship important in West African village life?

---

**diviner**

(dĭ-vīn´ər)

a person who communicated with the spirit world and helped people interact with their gods

**ancestor worship**
(ăn´sĕs´tər wûr´shĭp)

honor and reverence for ancestors, along with the belief that they can influence the gods

**kinship**
(kĭn´shĭp´)

the relationship among family members

---

# Chapter Overview
## Central and Southern Africa

**Fill in the blank spaces below with information from the chapter.**

**When:**
500 B.C.–A.D. 1700

**Where:**
Central and Southern Africa

**Who:**
Bantu speakers and other Africans

## Central and Southern Africa

### The Spread of Bantu

From where: _____

To where: _____

⬇

### The Rise of Coastal Trading States

The "people of the shore": _____

⬇

### The Rise of the Zimbabwe State

Zimbabwe's riches: _____

⬇

### The Kongo Kingdom

Traded goods: _____

Reading Support Resources

CHAPTER 6

# Lesson 1 Preview
## The Spread of Bantu

(*Across the Centuries* pp. 136–139)

### Migrations of Bantu-speaking Peoples

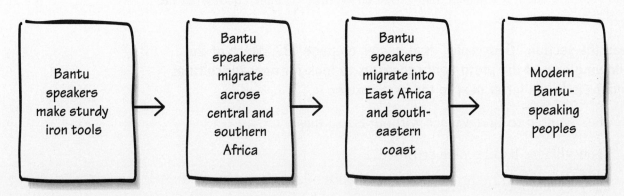

Bantu speakers make sturdy iron tools → Bantu speakers migrate across central and southern Africa → Bantu speakers migrate into East Africa and south-eastern coast → Modern Bantu-speaking peoples

1. **Look at the graphic organizer above. Then read and answer the following questions:**

   a. After Bantu speakers made sturdy tools, to where did they first migrate?

   _____

   b. To where did Bantu speakers next migrate?

   _____

   c. The final box on the right identifies what group of Bantu-speaking peoples?

   _____

2. **Look at the map on page 137 in your text. What kept the Bantu speakers from migrating north?**

   _____

   _____

CHAPTER 6
# Lesson 1 Reading Strategy
## The Spread of Bantu

(*Across the Centuries* pp. 136–139)

**Cause and Effect** This reading strategy helps you understand events and why they occur. As you read, think about the factors that caused an event. Then think about what the effects of that event may be.

1. **Read the section "Geography" that begins on page 137. Which of the following caused the proto-Bantu speakers to look for new agricultural lands? Circle the letter next to the best answer.**

   a. They wanted to find a place without tsetse flies.

   b. Their villages had become crowded.

   c. They were hunter-gatherers.

2. **Read the first two paragraphs under the heading "The Spread of Bantu Culture on page 138. Which of the following was an effect of their ability to make iron? Circle the letter next to the best answer.**

   a. Using iron made them more efficient at fishing and farming.

   b. Having iron weapons gave them military strength.

   c. Iron weapons were so good, they abandoned agriculture.

3. **As you read the lesson, complete the sentences below with causes and effects of certain events.**

   a. Migrants learned to avoid areas infested with tsetse flies, which can cause a disease called _____.

   b. Swahili, Luba, and Kongo are examples of languages that are a result of the migrations of the _____ speaking peoples.

   c. The migrants changed the ways of life of the people they met. They learned new words from each other as well as _____.

Summary also on Audiotape

# Lesson 1 Summary
## The Spread of Bantu

(*Across the Centuries* pp. 136–139)

**Thinking Focus:** How did the spread of the Bantu-speaking peoples affect the peoples of central and southern Africa?

## Geography

The Bantu languages are a group of languages within one of the four major language families of east, central, and southern Africa. Scholars who study **ethnolinguistics** say that proto-Bantu was the root language of all the Bantu languages. Proto-Bantu was the first language spoken by a people who once lived in West Africa in what is now eastern Nigeria or Cameroon. The speakers of proto-Bantu are thought to be the ancestors of different groups of people living in east, central, and southern Africa today.

Between 500 B.C. and A.D. 200, some of the villages where proto-Bantu speakers lived became crowded. Some people chose to **migrate** to find more farmland. For the next 2,000 years, descendants of the original proto-Bantu speakers continued migrating across east, central, and southern Africa.

The proto-Bantu speakers moved to three geographic areas.

- the Congo Basin
- the savannas of central and southern Africa
- the Great Rift Valley

Some people traveled down the Congo River to the rain forests of the Congo Basin. Some moved to central and southern Africa. There they found grassy areas good for raising cattle. Others traveled east to the Great Rift Valley. This rich valley had dry grasslands and a good water supply. From this area, people could travel north or south, or back to the Congo Basin.

**?** To which three geographic regions in east, central, and southern Africa did proto-Bantu speakers migrate and why?

**ethnolinguistics**
(ĕth´nō-lĭng-gwĭs´tĭks)
the gathering of information about various peoples through the study of their languages

**migrate**
(mī´grāt)
to move from one area to settle in another

*Summary continues on next page*

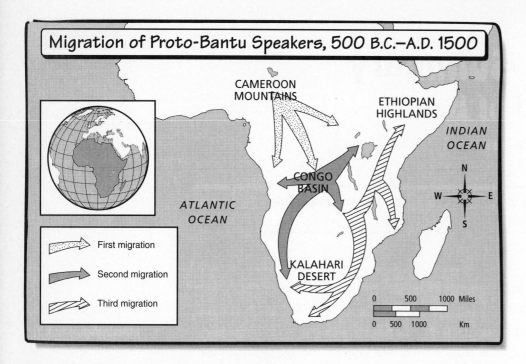

## The Spread of Bantu Culture

About 2,000 years ago, proto-Bantu-speaking people lived in what is today the eastern part of Nigeria. They made strong iron tools, which they used to clear land to grow crops.

As the proto-Bantu speakers migrated, many of the local groups learned the newcomers' farming methods and language. The Bantu-speaking people also took on the lifestyles of the local people they met. In the Congo Basin rain forests, the Bantu-speaking people followed the example of the local people and began fishing. From the East African peoples, Bantu speakers learned to grow crops like bananas, coconuts, sugar cane, and rice. By 1400, Bantu-speaking groups lived in much of sub-Saharan Africa.

**[?]** How did migration change the lives of the Bantu speakers and the people they met?

## Society of the Bantu Speakers

The family was the most common political structure among Bantu speakers. Families and clans formed villages. These villages were most often led by one man or a small group of elders. Some villages were part of a larger state, kingdom, or empire.

**[?]** Describe the most common political structure among the Bantu-speaking groups.

CHAPTER 6

# Lesson 2 Preview
## The Rise of Coastal Trading States

(*Across the Centuries* pp. 141–144)

### African Trading Ports

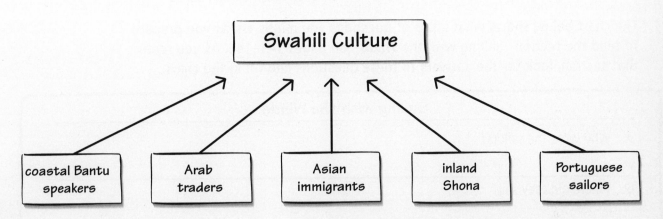

1. **Look at the graphic organizer above. Then read the following sentences and fill in the blanks.**

   a. Arab _____ were an influence on Swahili culture.

   b. Asian immigrants were also an influence on _____ culture.

2. **Study the map showing trade routes on page 142 in your text. Then use the map to answer the following questions:**

   a. What color is used to show trade routes?

   _____

   b. Name three products that came from India.

   _____

   _____

   c. Across what ocean did traders travel to get from Hormuz to Kilwa?

   _____

**CHAPTER 6**

# Lesson 2 Reading Strategy
## The Rise of Coastal Trading States

*(Across the Centuries* pp. 141–144)

**Self-Question** This reading strategy helps you stay focused on what you read. Ask yourself questions before you read a section. Then read to find the answer to your questions.

1. **The chart below shows what kinds of questions you might ask as you prepare to read the section "Sailing with the Winds" on pages 141–142. As you read that section, look for the answers to these questions and fill in the chart.**

| Sailing with the Winds | |
| --- | --- |
| A. Who were the sailors? | |
| B. Where did they sail? | |
| C. What was the importance of the winds? | |

2. **Read the heading "The Rise of City-States" on pages 142–143. Which question below would you expect to have answered by reading these pages?**
   a. How did city-states' rulers increase their wealth?
   b. What language did the Shona speak?
   c. What kind of fish could be found in the Indian Ocean?

   **Read the section to see if the question you chose was answered. If it was, write the answer to the question.**

   _____

3. **Read the heading "From Riches to Ruin" on page 143 and read the first paragraph beneath the heading. Write a question in the space below that you expect might be answered as you read the section.**

   _____

4. **Now, read the entire section "From Riches to Ruin" on pages 143–144 and look for the answer to your question. Write your answer in the space below.**

   _____
   _____

# Lesson 2 Summary
## The Rise of Coastal Trading States

(*Across the Centuries* pp. 141–144)

---

**Thinking Focus:** How did East Africa become part of an international trade network?

## Sailing with the Winds

By about 200 B.C., traders crisscrossed the Indian Ocean between East Africa, Arabia, India, Ceylon, and the East Indies. This network developed because Arab traders learned to make use of seasonal winds called **monsoons**. These winds changed direction with the seasons. Between November and March the winds from the northeast monsoon carried Arab traders sailing in ships called dhows down the East African coast. In April, the winds came from the southwest, and the Arab traders sailed home.

Bantu-speaking Africans traded goods with Arab merchants. Over time, some Arab traders married into African families. The traders' Arabian, Persian, and Indonesian cultures mixed with that of the Bantu speakers. This mixture produced the Swahili culture and language. Swahili-speaking people still live throughout east and central Africa.

**monsoon**
(mŏn-sōōn´)
a kind of wind that regularly changes direction with the seasons

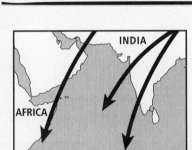

### Monsoons

**November to March**
winds blow from Asia toward Africa

prevailing wind direction

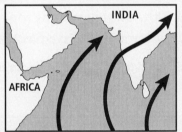
**April to October**
winds blow from the Indian Ocean off Africa toward India

[?] Describe the monsoons and explain why they were so important to the Indian Ocean trade network.

*Summary continues on next page*

## The Rise of City-States

In the hundreds of Swahili fishing and farming villages along the coast, the people developed a complex economic system. Both women and men served as traders. The Swahili were a link between foreign traders and the inland Africans, or people who lived farther away from the coast. One inland group was the Shona, who lived in what is now Zimbabwe. The Shona mined gold and other metals from the land.

By 1100, the Shona were bringing these valuable metals to coastal trading towns to trade them for foreign goods. Other inland Africans brought ivory, grain, and sometimes slaves to trade for foreign goods like knives, farming tools, and fabrics. People could become very rich through trade. Competition developed among merchants of the various trading-port towns. Each group of coastal merchants tried to attract the largest amount of business.

Many of these trading-port towns became **city-states**. The rulers of the city-states grew wealthy from the city-states' trade.

[?]  Describe a typical East African trading town of the 1300s.

**city-state**
(sĭtē-stāt´)

an independent state made up of a city and the land that surrounds it

## From Riches to Ruin

The trading towns and city-states thrived during the 1300s and 1400s. In 1498, the Portuguese explorer Vasco da Gama arrived. The Portuguese government wanted him to find a trade route in order to control the Far East spice trade. But Vasco da Gama realized that controlling East Africa trade would be very profitable. In 1505, the Portuguese attacked and destroyed Kilwa, Mombasa, and other city-states. The Portuguese then tried to monopolize trade in East African ports. By the late 1500s, Swahili groups took back control of some ports. But the cities never again thrived as they once had.

[?]  Who caused the destruction of many East African trading centers, and why?

CHAPTER 6

# Lesson 3 Preview
## The Rise of the Zimbabwe State

(*Across the Centuries* pp. 145–148)

### The Zimbabwe State

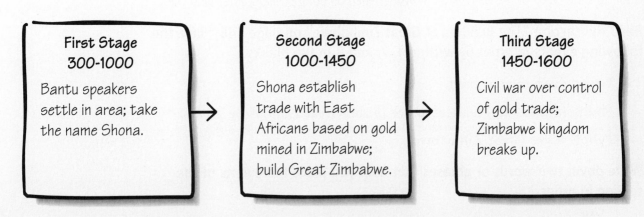

**First Stage
300-1000**

Bantu speakers settle in area; take the name Shona.

→

**Second Stage
1000-1450**

Shona establish trade with East Africans based on gold mined in Zimbabwe; build Great Zimbabwe.

→

**Third Stage
1450-1600**

Civil war over control of gold trade; Zimbabwe kingdom breaks up.

1. **Look at the graphic organizer above. Then read the following list of events. Place the events in order according to which happened first, second, and third.**

___ Shona build Great Zimbabwe.

___ Bantu speakers settle in the area.

___ The kingdom of Zimbabwe breaks up.

2. **Read the lesson title and the red and blue headings in your text on pages 145–148. Use words from those headings to fill in the lesson outline below.**

The Rise of the Zimbabwe State

   I. The _____ of Great Zimbabwe

   II. The _____ Mines of _____

      A. The _____ for Gold

      B. The Gold _____

   III. The _____ of Zimbabwe

CHAPTER 6
# Lesson 3 Reading Strategy
## The Rise of the Zimbabwe State

(*Across the Centuries* pp. 145–148)

**Sequence** This reading strategy helps you follow the order of events. As you read, pay attention to dates and times, as well as to words such as *before, finally, after,* and *then.*

1. **Read the section "The Builders of Great Zimbabwe" on page 146. Place the following events in order by writing 1, 2, and 3 in the blanks.**

   —— Great Zimbabwe is built.

   —— Shona farmers and herders arrive in the Great Zimbabwe area.

   —— People leave Great Zimbabwe.

2. **Write down two words or phrases that help you place the events of the section in order.**

   _____

   _____

   _____

   _____

3. **Read the section "The Gold Mines of Zimbabwe" on pages 147–148. Place the following events in order by writing 1, 2, and 3 in the blanks.**

   ___ The rulers of Zimbabwe control most of the country between the Limpopo and Zambezi Rivers.

   ___ Archaeologists find more than 60,000 mine shafts on the Zimbabwe Plateau.

   ___ In the 1100s, the Shona begin digging shafts to mine gold.

# Lesson 3 Summary
## The Rise of the Zimbabwe State

*(Across the Centuries* pp. 145–148)

**Thinking Focus:** Describe some of the ways the Shona benefited from their decision to settle on the site now known as the Zimbabwe Plateau.

## The Builders of Great Zimbabwe

Sometime between A.D. 1100 and 1300, the Bantu-speaking Shona built a huge stone city called Great Zimbabwe. Today only ruins remain of the stone walls and buildings that covered almost 200 acres.

People lived at Great Zimbabwe long before the walls were built. The Shona chose to settle the area because the **plateau** had enough rainfall for growing crops. The earth also held large deposits of granite, iron, copper, and gold. By the late 1100s, the Shona had developed their own state, based on farming, cattle herding, mining, metalworking, and trade.

The Shona used their riches to buy resources and to extend their power. But Great Zimbabwe fell into a decline. Some scientists believe that years of bad harvests or low rainfall was the cause. Also, too much cattle grazing may have ruined the soil. Eventually, people left Great Zimbabwe for better land.

**plateau**
(plă-tō´)
a raised piece of land that is fairly flat

| Great Zimbabwe | | |
|---|---|---|
| **Beginning** | **Height** | **Decline** |
| good rainfall, minerals | farming, herding, mining, trade | drought, poor crops, worn-out land |

[?] Trace the growth and decline of Great Zimbabwe.

*Summary continues on next page*

# The Gold Mines of Zimbabwe

At first the Bantu-speaking Shona people didn't value gold more than they did other metals, such as copper and iron. In fact, they found iron more useful because it was stronger than gold. But gold was highly valued by coastal traders.

In the 1100s, the Shona began to dig for gold. They built mines on the Zimbabwe Plateau. Through mining and trading, Zimbabwe became a very rich and powerful kingdom. By the 1400s, the rulers of Zimbabwe had expanded their kingdom greatly. They controlled most of the country between the Limpopo River in the south to the Zambezi on the north and from the Indian Ocean west to the Kalahari Desert. Great Zimbabwe was the capital and center of trade. Scholars have learned much about the Shona's past from studying the Shona's rich **oral tradition.**

[?] How did Zimbabwe become a wealthy and powerful kingdom?

# The Breakup of Zimbabwe

In about 1450, the chiefs of Zimbabwe's gold-mining areas declared their independence from Great Zimbabwe. A group led by King Mwene Mutapa formed a new empire called Monomutapa. In 1490, civil wars weakened Monomutapa, and by the early 1500s, the empire was split.

During this time, Portuguese traders tried to take control of Monomutapa's trade and gold mines. They wanted to increase their wealth and power. In 1570, they attacked the empire. For 100 years the Portuguese tried to take control of Monomutapa. But the Portuguese forces lost so many soldiers to **malaria** that they never completely conquered Monomutapa. Monomutapa, however, had been seriously weakened by wars. By the late 1600s, southern kingdoms took control of Monomutapa.

[?] Why did the Portuguese undermine Monomutapa?

**oral tradition**
(ŏr´əl trə-dĭsh´ən)
the history, legends, and beliefs that a culture passes from generation to generation by word of mouth

**malaria**
(mə-lâr´ē-ə)
a disease carried by a certain type of mosquito

**CHAPTER 6**

# Lesson 4 Preview
## The Kongo Kingdom

(*Across the Centuries* pp. 149–153)

### The Kongo Trade

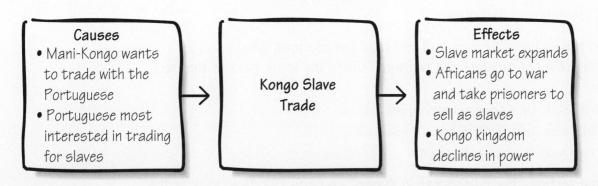

**Causes**
- Mani-Kongo wants to trade with the Portuguese
- Portuguese most interested in trading for slaves

Kongo Slave Trade

**Effects**
- Slave market expands
- Africans go to war and take prisoners to sell as slaves
- Kongo kingdom declines in power

1. **Look at the graphic organizer above. Then use the following words to fill in the blanks below.**

   | kingdom | slave | Kongo | Portuguese |
   |---------|-------|-------|------------|

   a. One of the causes of the _____ slave trade was the Mani-Kongo's willingness to trade with the _____.

   b. One of the effects of the Kongo _____ trade was that the Kongo _____ declined in power.

2. **Look at the graph on page 153 in your text. Then answer the following questions:**

   a. Approximately how many slaves were exported in 1500?

   _____

   b. Around what year were the greatest number of slaves traded?

   _____

CHAPTER 6

# Lesson 4 Reading Strategy
## The Kongo Kingdom

(*Across the Centuries* pp. 149–153)

**Using the Visuals** This reading strategy helps you to use photographs, maps, charts, and illustrations to help you to understand what you read. As you read, be sure to study the visuals and carefully read the captions.

1. **Look at the pictures on page 150 and read the captions. What can you conclude from the pictures and captions? Circle the letter next to the best answer.**

   a. The people of Kongo were Christians.

   b. Wood was one of the Kongo's resources.

   c. Kongo was far from the ocean.

2. **Read the section "The Portuguese in Kongo" on page 152. Then look at the ivory carving on page 152. Do you think the Portuguese explorers were prepared to fight the Africans if necessary? Use clues from the carving to support your answer.**

   _____

   _____

3. **Look at the picture at the top of page 153 and read the caption. Use information from the picture and the caption to fill in the chart below.**

| | |
|---|---|
| A. Who are the people on the left side of the picture? | |
| B. Who is the woman in the middle of the picture? | |
| C. Why is she revered in Angola today? | |

# Lesson 4 Summary
## The Kongo Kingdom

(*Across the Centuries* pp. 149–153)

Summary also on
Audiotape

---

**Thinking Focus:** How did Kongo change after the arrival of the Portuguese?

## The Growth of Kongo

In the early 1300s, two Bantu-speaking clans joined together to form what became the kingdom of Kongo. By the 1400s, Kongo's king, the Mani-Kongo, ruled about two million people. The kingdom was made up of farmers and traders and was quite wealthy.

Kongo's capital was Mbanza. It was about 100 miles east of the Atlantic Ocean and about 50 miles south of the Congo River. Farmers planted crops like millet and sorghum. Mbanza was also a trade center. Kongo people traded salt, iron, and ivory. As **currency,** or money, they used small seashells. When they began trading with the Portuguese, the Portuguese wanted gold as payment. The Kongo region had no gold, so the Portuguese asked the Mani-Kongo to give them slaves as payment.

? Describe the early development of Kongo.

## The Portuguese in Kongo

In 1490, the Portuguese king sent **missionaries** to educate the Mani-Kongo. The missionaries converted the Mani-Kongo to Christianity. Later, his son became king and took the Christian name Affonso I.

The connection between the Kongo and Portugal remained strong until the early 1500s. By that time, Portugal had begun to send Portuguese settlers to the island of São Tomé, 250 miles off of the Kongo coast. The Portuguese governor of São Tomé found that sugar grew well on the island. He set up large farms called **plantations.** He wanted to make as much money as possible from the plantations. For this reason, he decided to have slaves work the fields.

**currency**
(kûr´ən-sē)
any form of money

**missionary**
(mĭsh´ə-nĕr´ē)
a person sent to a foreign country to do religious work

**plantation**
(plăn-tā´shən)
a large farm where crops are grown

*Summary continues
on next page*

At first, Affonso sent him slaves. In Africa slavery was accepted. But slaves in Africa were treated well and could earn their freedom. The Portuguese had very different ideas about slavery. Often slaves were worked to death.

**?**  What European nation led in the African slave trade?

## Slaves, Guns, and Civil War

The Portuguese found that selling slaves was very profitable. Traditionally, Africans took prisoners during wars and made them slaves. The Portuguese got villages to declare war on each other in order to get more slaves. They even gave villagers guns.

In 1526, Affonso wrote a letter to Portugal's King John to beg the king to stop the slave trade. The king did nothing. By the 1600s, the Kongo kingdom was breaking apart. The Portuguese had urged Kongo chiefs to rebel against the Mani-Kongo. Civil wars broke out as villages raided each other to capture people to sell as slaves.

The Kongo's contact with the Portuguese had long-lasting effects on all of Africa. The Portuguese destroyed Kongo's trade in goods and replaced it with trade in human beings. Finally, the civil wars sparked by the Portuguese brought an end to the Kongo kingdom.

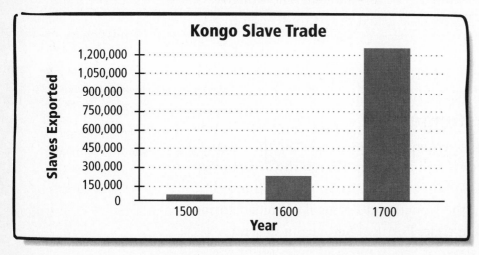

**?**  Why did civil war erupt in Kongo?

# Chapter Overview
## Three Empires

Fill in the blanks below with information from the chapter.

| When: |
| --- |
| 997 – 1923 |
| Who: |
| Mongols, Ottomans, Indians |

## The Empire Builders

**Three Empires, 997 – 1923**

### The Mongol Empire

**Who:** Nomadic herders

**Where from:** _____
_____
_____
_____

**When:** _____
_____
_____

### The Ottoman Empire

**First leader:** _____
_____

**Where they settled:** _____
_____
_____
_____

**When:** Beginning around 1300; ends in 1923

### The Mughal Empire

**Founder:** _____
_____

**Where:** Almost all of India, except the far south

**When:** _____
_____
_____

**CHAPTER 7**

# Lesson 1 Preview
## The Mongols

*(Across the Centuries pp. 162–169)*

### The Mongol Empire

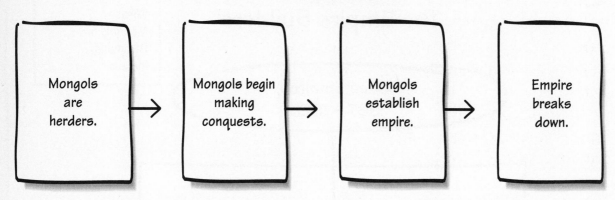

1. **Look at the graphic organizer above. Then read the following sentences and fill in the blanks.**

   a. The Mongols started out as _____ .

   b. According to the flow chart, what was the last thing to happen to the Mongol Empire?

   _____

2. **Look at the map on page 166. What trade route is shown by the red line?**

   _____

   _____

CHAPTER 7

# Lesson 1 Reading Strategy
## The Mongols

(*Across the Centuries* pp. 162–169)

**Finding the Main Idea** This reading strategy helps you organize and remember what you read. When you finish a selection, jot down the main idea and its supporting details.

1. **Read the section "The Life of Mongol Nomads" on pages 162–164. Which sentence below best expresses the main idea of the section? Circle the letter next to the best answer.**
   a. The summers were very hot and the winters were very long on the steppes.
   b. The Mongols were nomadic people who competed for grazing land for their herds.
   c. Mongols traveled in family groups called clans.

2. **Read the section "The Great Khan" on pages 164–165. Which sentence below best expresses the main idea of the section? Circle the letter next to the best answer.**
   a. Genghis Khan's real name was Temujin.
   b. When Genghis Khan was 12 years old, his father was killed.
   c. Genghis Khan's reputation as a leader helped him get elected ruler of the Mongols.

3. **Read the section "Genghis Khan the Warrior" on page 165. Then write the main idea of the section below.**

   _____

   **Next write two supporting details for the main idea.**

   _____

   _____

# Lesson 1 Summary
## The Mongols

(*Across the Centuries* pp. 162–169)

Summary also on
Audiotape

---

**Thinking Focus:** How did the Mongols affect Europe and Asia?

## The Life of Mongol Nomads

A group of people called the Mongols lived in the **steppes** of Central
Asia. This is an area of harsh plains. The steppes had very few trees.
The weather there was very hot and dry in the summer, and very cold
in the winter. The Mongols raised sheep and horses. They moved
around in order to find grassland to feed their animals. They slept in
tents that were easy to put up and take down. The Mongols lived in
large family groups called **clans**. Several clans together made up a tribe.
Tribes often had to fight each other to have grazing land. The
Mongols became very good horseback riders so that they could
protect themselves and fight for land.

**?** What effect did the environment of the steppes have on the Mongol people?

**steppe**
(stěp)
a dry, grassy plain

**clan**
(klăn)
a group of families that
come from a common
ancestor

**khan**
(kän)
a Mongol ruler

## Mongol Leadership

Mongol horses helped the soldiers by carrying food and water. This
meant that the Mongols could ride great distances quickly. They did
not need to stop often for supplies.

There was often fighting between clans and tribes. One leader, or
**khan,** who was able to bring the tribes together was Genghis Khan. He
turned the Mongol warriors into a powerful army. He organized them
and made a system of signals to help the troops communicate with
each other. Genghis Khan took over a large area of land. His empire
stretched from the Sea of Japan to the Caspian Sea.

Genghis Kahn respected the knowledge and beliefs of others. He
knew that the Mongols needed a written language, so he told one of
his war prisoners to make one up. Genghis Khan also used the skills
of others to make his army better. Genghis Khan also opened up his
empire to foreign travelers. He made laws to stop the Mongol tribes
from fighting with each other.

**?** What qualities did Genghis Khan possess that made him a successful ruler?

*Summary continues
on next page*

## The Later Khans

Genghis Khan died in 1227. His empire was divided among his four sons. Twenty years later, one of Genghis Khan's grandsons, Kublai Khan, was made ruler of the Mongol Empire. Under his leadership, the Mongols took more and more land. Kublai Khan started many new programs. He encouraged local and long-distance trade. This helped imports and exports to grow. He also set up a postal system that helped communication and trade. But the Mongol Empire grew too large to control. The Mongols also began to take on the customs and religions of the people they conquered. By 1300, the empire's unity was gone. This made it easier for enemies to attack. By 1447, the Mongol Empire had lost its power.

**?** Support the following statement with details: The Mongols were better conquerors than rulers.

## The Impact of the Mongols

The Mongols were not only good warriors. They did many other good things. They believed there was truth in every religion and encouraged religious freedom. They supported trade and travel. People from many different places visited Mongol lands. In this way, new ideas spread from Asia to Europe. One visitor was an Italian named Marco Polo. Stories about his visit were the first complete and factual record of China to reach Europe.

**?** What were the positive effects of Mongol rule?

**CHAPTER 7**

# Lesson 2 Preview
## The Ottoman Empire

*(Across the Centuries pp. 170–177)*

### The Ottoman Empire

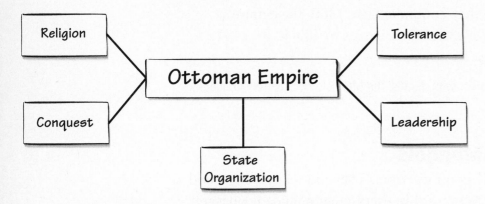

1. **Look at the graphic organizer above. Then read the following sentences and fill in the blanks.**

   a. The graphic shows important information about the

   _____ .

   b. Name three things the empire was known for.

   _____

   _____

   _____

2. **Study the map on page 171. During what years did the Ottoman Empire reach its greatest size?**

   _____

CHAPTER 7
# Lesson 2 Reading Strategy
## The Ottoman Empire

(*Across the Centuries* pp. 170–177)

**Self-Question** This reading strategy helps you stay focused on what you read. Ask yourself questions before you read a section. Then read to see if you can find the answer to your questions.

1. **Look at the map on page 171 and read the caption. Which question below asks about information on this map? Circle the letter next to the best answer.**

   a. What kind of people were the Ottoman Turks?

   b. When did the Ottoman Empire expand into Egypt?

   c. What was the life of a slave like during the early Ottoman Empire?

2. **Read the heading "The Early Ottoman Empire" on page 171. Which question below do you expect to have answered in the paragraphs that follow this heading? Circle the letter next to the best answer.**

   a. How did the Ottoman Empire begin?

   b. How did the Ottoman Empire end?

   c. What do other cultures think of the Ottoman Empire?

3. **Now read the section "The Early Ottoman Empire" to see if the question you chose is answered. If it was, write the answer to the question.**

   _____

   _____

   _____

   _____

# Lesson 2 Summary
## The Ottoman Empire

(*Across the Centuries* pp. 170–177)

**Thinking Focus:** How important a factor was leadership in the rise and fall of the Ottoman Empire?

## The Early Ottoman Empire

The Mongols took over most of Central Asia in the 1200s. They drove many Turkish tribes out. Many of these tribes were Muslim, believers in Islam. These Muslims settled in Asia Minor and set up small states. One Muslim state was run by a chief named Osman. He and his followers were **ghazis** who fought to bring Islam to others. Osman's armies defeated and brought together lands that had been part of the Byzantine Empire. This was the beginning of the Ottoman Empire. As it continued to grow, the Ottoman Empire became a danger to European Christians, who put together an army to stop the Muslims. But the Ottoman forces defeated the Christians in 1326 at Kosovo, in the former Yugoslavia.

? How did the Ottoman Empire begin and expand?

## Rulers and Subjects

The ruler of the Ottoman Empire was called the **sultan**. He was helped by the **grand vizier,** or **prime minister.** The grand vizier was in charge of the **divan,** the group that made laws. **Janissaries** were slaves of the sultan, but they often rose to great importance. They were taken as boys between the ages of eight and fourteen, and were sent to Istanbul to be educated. Some were trained for military service, others for government work. Most were Christians who were converted to Islam. Many janissaries became powerful and rich. Some even ran the government and army.

Ottoman rulers tried to treat non-Muslims fairly. Non-Muslims had to pay a tax so that they could practice their religion. They lived in partly self-governed groups called **millets**. This system helped the Ottoman Empire to have peace for many years.

? What highly successful political and educational structures did the Ottoman Empire develop?

**ghazi**
(gä′zē)
a Muslim warrior

**sultan**
(sŭl′tən)
the ruler of a Muslim country

**grand vizier**
(grănd vĭ-zîr′)
the prime minister who advises the sultan

**divan**
(dĭ-văn′)
a governing group in the Ottoman Empire

**janissary**
(jăn′ĭ-sĕrē)
slave/soldier in Ottoman Empire

**millet**
(mĭl′ā)
a partly self-governing group of non-Muslim people in the Ottoman Empire

*Summary continues on next page*

Reading Support Resources

## The Empire at Its Height

In 1453, the Ottoman Turks captured the Byzantine city of Constantinople. They renamed it Istanbul and made it their new capital. Istanbul became an important center of trade.

The Ottoman Empire reached its height from 1520 to 1566 under the rule of Suleiman. He led one of the richest, largest, and most powerful empires in the world. Suleiman made laws that were fair to both Muslims and non-Muslims. He was also responsible for huge building programs throughout the empire. Suleiman supported the writing of poetry, which became very important in the empire.

**?** What were Suleiman's accomplishments?

## Decline of the Ottoman Empire

In the centuries after Suleiman, the Ottoman Empire began to lose its lands and military power. The empire's economic strength depended on constant growth. When growth slowed in 1571, so did the income from conquered lands. The empire also declined because another trade route to the East was discovered. The old trade route through Ottoman land became less important. As trade decreased, so did the money the empire earned. Finally, the janissaries started to play a bigger role in government and fought among themselves for power. All of these things caused the government to weaken.

**?** Why did the Ottoman Empire decline?

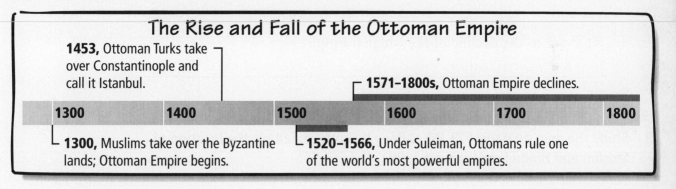

### The Rise and Fall of the Ottoman Empire

**1453,** Ottoman Turks take over Constantinople and call it Istanbul.

**1571–1800s,** Ottoman Empire declines.

| 1300 | 1400 | 1500 | 1600 | 1700 | 1800 |

**1300,** Muslims take over the Byzantine lands; Ottoman Empire begins.

**1520–1566,** Under Suleiman, Ottomans rule one of the world's most powerful empires.

CHAPTER 7

# Lesson 3 Preview
## The Mughal Empire

(*Across the Centuries* pp. 178–185)

### Mughal India

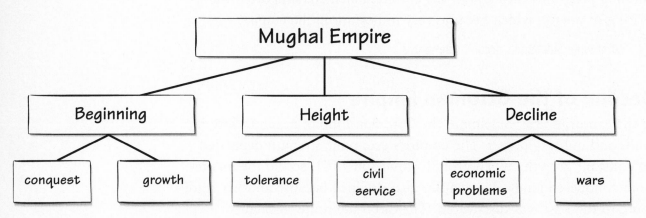

1. **Look at the graphic organizer above. Then read the following sentences and fill in the blanks.**

   a. What were two important parts of the Mughal Empire at its height?

   _____

   _____

   b. What led to the decline of the Mughal Empire?

   _____

   _____

2. **Study the map on page 179. What does it show you about the location of Muslim and Hindu lands around 1500?**

   _____

   _____

   _____

   _____

   _____

CHAPTER 7

# Lesson 3 Reading Strategy
## The Mughal Empire

(*Across the Centuries* pp. 178–185)

**Using the Visuals** This reading strategy asks you to use photographs, maps, charts, and illustrations to help you understand what you read. As you read, be sure to study the visuals and carefully read the captions.

1. **Look at the picture on page 178 and read the caption. What can you tell about India's land from this picture? Circle the letter next to the best answer.**

   a. India is partly desert.

   b. India has both mountains and farmland.

   c. India has more rainfall than China.

2. **Use the map on page 179 to find out which region has the highest elevation? Circle the letter next to the best answer.**

   a. India

   b. Persia

   c. Tibet

3. **Study the map on page 183. Then fill out the chart on the expansion of the Mughal Empire.**

| Who | What |
|-----|------|
| a. | He took the most land for the Mughal Empire. |
| b. | He took the least land for the Mughal Empire but was its founder. |
| c. | He ruled until 1605. |
| d. | He expanded the Mughal Empire south of the Krishna River. |

# Lesson 3 Summary
## The Mughal Empire
*(Across the Centuries pp. 178–185)*

**Thinking Focus:** What factors contributed to the rise and fall of the Mughal Empire?

## On the Eve of the Empire

The Himalayas curve across the northern part of India. To the south is an area with some of the richest farmland in the world, the Indus and Ganges river valleys. Farther south is the Deccan plateau, which has many rugged mountains and rivers. Few invaders came this far south. But in the north there was always a struggle for the land. By the early 1500s, Muslim invaders had taken over some Indian cities. Other cities stayed in the control of Hindu princes. The Hindus found a way to live with Muslims by making a place for Muslims in their ruling class.

**?** In what ways was northern India a divided country during the 1500s?

## Founders of the Empire

In 1517, an army led by a Muslim Turk named Babur invaded India. Later, Babur founded the Mughal Empire. He was a wise and fair leader. Babur's grandson, Akbar, became emperor in 1556. Akbar worked to bring the Hindus into the government. He made the empire's tax system more fair and ended the tax on non-Muslims. He also divided the land into provinces and gave jobs to the people who would do the best job running the provinces. Workers were paid by **salary,** or fixed payment, without regard for religion.

**?** Evaluate this statement: Akbar was a just and tolerant Mughal emperor.

**salary**
(săl′ə-rē)
a fixed, regular payment for services

*Summary continues on next page*

## Inheritors of the Empire

In 1605, Akbar's oldest son, Jahangir, came to power. He continued Akbar's plan to expand the empire. He also started programs to rebuild schools and religious buildings.

Jahangir's son, Shah Jahan, ruled from 1628 to 1658. He became famous for the large amounts of money he spent on construction projects. One project was the Taj Mahal. It was built with marble, rare and colorful jewels, pointed arches, and domes. Under Shah Jahan's rule, the empire got larger. But his military projects and building programs took a lot of money and weakened the empire's economy.

**?** How did the rule of Jahangir and Shah Jahan affect the empire?

## End of the Empire

Aurangzeb, Shah Jahan's son, was the last Mughal emperor to expand the empire. He brought back the tax on non-Muslims and did not let Hindus build temples. He tried to force the Hindus to become Muslims. The Hindus rebelled against him.

As the Mughal empire weakened, Europeans saw their chance to get more control in the region. They wanted India's pepper, spices and fine cotton cloth. They forced their own trade rules on the Mughals. In the 1700s, a trading company from Great Britain took over the rule of an Indian province. By 1858, Great Britain had gotten rid of the last Mughal emperor.

**?** Why did the Mughal Empire decline?

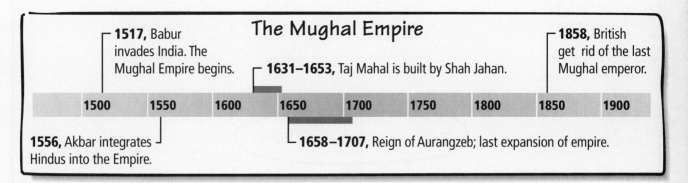

The Mughal Empire

**1517**, Babur invades India. The Mughal Empire begins.

**1631–1653**, Taj Mahal is built by Shah Jahan.

**1858**, British get rid of the last Mughal emperor.

1500 1550 1600 1650 1700 1750 1800 1850 1900

**1556**, Akbar integrates Hindus into the Empire.

**1658–1707**, Reign of Aurangzeb; last expansion of empire.

# Chapter Overview
## China

Fill in the blanks below with information
from the chapter.

**When:**
220 –1912

**Who:**
Chinese

## China Through the Centuries

An Emerging Empire

Years of
Disorder

Spread of
_____

_____
of China

The Flowering of
Chinese Culture

• Promotions based
on _____

• improved roads and
_____

• movable type
_____

China and the Larger World

• _____
invade from the north

• Ming _____

• _____ invade,
set up Qing dynasty

CHAPTER 8

# Lesson 1 Preview

## An Emerging Empire

(*Across the Centuries* pp. 192–197)

### China After the Han Dynasty

|  | Period of Disorder | Sui Dynasty |
|---|---|---|
| **Religion** | Buddhism | Buddhism, Confucianism, and Daoism |
| **Government** | nomads in North; landowners in South | new administrative system |
| **Economy** | South expands | Grand Canal built |

1. **Look at the graphic organizer above. Read each sentence. Write a *D* in the blank to identify the sentence about the period of disorder. Write an *S* in the blank to identify the Sui Dynasty.**

   ___ The economy in the south expands.

   ___ There is a new administrative system of government.

2. **Look at the headings on pages 193, 194, and 195. Then complete the following summary with words from the headings.**

   a. After the Han Dynasty fell, China endured years of _____.

   b. Many people turned to the teachings of _____ for comfort.

   c. Then Yang Jian declared himself Emperor. He undertook the

      _____ of China.

CHAPTER 8

# Lesson 1 Reading Strategy
## An Emerging Empire

(*Across the Centuries* pp. 192–197)

**Using the Visuals** This reading strategy asks you to use photographs, maps, charts, and illustrations to help you understand what you read. As you read, be sure to study the visuals and carefully read the captions.

**Use the map and its caption on page 193 to answer the next two questions.**

1. **What body of water does the Huang He flow into? Circle the letter next to the best answer.**
   a. Chang Jiang
   b. East China Sea
   c. Yellow Sea

2. **Trace the route of the Silk Road. Then complete the following sentence.**

   The Silk Road passed through the _____
   Mountains.

3. **Look at the photograph on page 195 and read the caption. Which of the following statements is true? Circle the letter next to the best answer.**
   a. The Buddha meditates while seated.
   b. Buddhism did not spread to China until after the 300s.
   c. The sculpture was made by the Buddha.

4. **Using only the pictures and captions in the lesson, find answers to the questions listed in the chart below. Include the page numbers where you found each answer.**

| Question | Answer | Page Number |
|---|---|---|
| a. Who taught manners to ladies of the Han emperor's court? | | |
| b. How long is the Great Wall? | | |
| c. What kind of land is the Great Wall build on? | | |

# Lesson 1 Summary
## An Emerging Empire

(*Across the Centuries* pp. 192–197)

**Thinking Focus:** What were some of the obstacles to unity in China, and how did Emperor Wen overcome them?

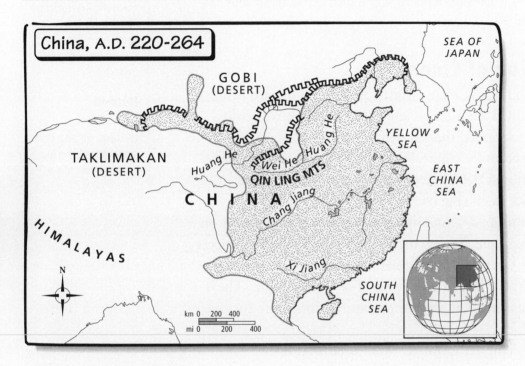

China, A.D. 220-264

## Years of Disorder

The Qin Ling mountains divide China into northern and southern regions. So, people living in northern and southern China had almost no contact with each other in early times. Then in 221 B.C., the Han dynasty united both regions.

Geography also protected China from invaders. The Himalayas and the Taklimakan Desert protected China in the west. The Yellow Sea and East China Sea protected China in the east. Only the northern plains were open to attack.

Invasions and other problems brought an end to the Han dynasty in A.D. 220. China was not unified for the next 360 years. In the south, large landowners controlled most local affairs. In the north, nomadic invaders set up a series of short-lived kingdoms.

[?] Support this statement: Geographic features made China difficult to unify.

*Summary continues on next page*

## The Spread of Buddhism

During the Han dynasty, most Chinese followed **Confucianism**. Confucianism taught people to study hard, respect their elders, and serve the government. But during the troubled times after the end of the Han dynasty, many people turned to **Buddhism**. Buddhism taught that people could escape suffering. Through meditation, they could enter a state of complete freedom and peace. The idea of escape from daily troubles appealed to people of all classes. By the 400s, Buddhist temples and monasteries were thriving throughout China.

**?** Why did the Chinese find Buddhism more appealing than Confucianism after the fall of the Han dynasty?

## The Reunification of China

More than 300 years after the Han dynasty ended, a northern official named Yang Jian reunited the Chinese empire. Yang Jian was called Emperor Wen, and he founded the Sui dynasty.

Emperor Wen helped unify China by restoring ancient traditions. For example, he promoted the Chinese tradition of learning. He preserved classic books by having clerks copy them by hand.

Emperor Wen also unified China by focusing people's attention on common goals. For example, he organized large public works projects such as rebuilding the Great Wall of China. He also began work on the Grand Canal between the Huang He and the Chang Jiang. The Grand Canal later became an important transportation route for people, grain, and silk.

To govern his huge empire, Emperor Wen organized his government into departments and offices. He established exams for public officials and hired inspectors to make sure people did their jobs.

Emperor Wen was a Buddhist, but he encouraged the ancient belief systems of Confucianism and **Daoism**. Daoists follow the teachings of Laozi, who urged people to live in harmony with nature and be content with their lives. Supporting all three teachings was another way that Emperor Wen promoted unity.

**?** What steps did Emperor Wen take to reunify China?

**Confucianism**
(kən-fyo͞o'shən-ĭz'ēm)

teachings by Confucius that promote study, respect for elders, and government service

**Buddhism**
(bo͞o'dĭz'əm)

a system of thought and practice that teaches that suffering is part of life, that life is a cycle of death and rebirth, and that suffering can be overcome

**Daoism**
(dou'ĭz'əm)

teachings of Laozi that emphasized living in harmony with nature

CHAPTER 8

# Lesson 2 Preview
## The Flowering of Chinese Culture

(*Across the Centuries* pp. 202–208)

### Chinese Cultural Achievements

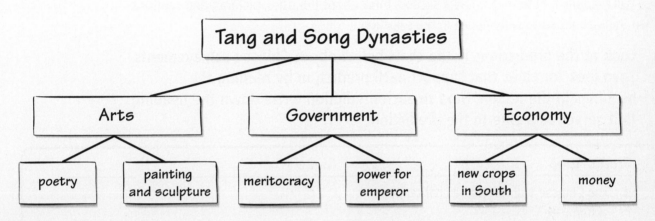

1. **Look at the graphic organizer above. Then read the following sentences and fill in the blanks.**

   a. The Tang and Song dynasties enjoyed achievements in poetry,

      _____, and _____.

   b. During the Tang and Song dynasties, the south prospered by

      introducing _____.

2. **Look at the headings on pages 203, 204, and 206. Then complete the following summary with words from the headings.**

   The Tang and Song emperors reformed the _____ system.

   They built roads and waterways. This supported the _____.
   New goods and inventions improved Chinese life. Yet the Chinese people

   retained respect for their _____.

CHAPTER 8
# Lesson 2 Reading Strategy
## The Flowering of Chinese Culture

(*Across the Centuries* pp. 202–208)

**Predict/Infer** This reading strategy helps you understand what you have read and what you will read next. Before you read a section, think about the titles, pictures, and captions. Then think about what will happen in the selection.

1. **Look at the predictions in the chart below about Chinese achievements. Then look for clues that support each prediction by reading the headings in the lesson. Next to each prediction write down the heading that serves as a clue to the prediction.**

| Predictions | Clues |
|---|---|
| a. The Chinese will develop a civil service system. | |
| b. Improved roads will help China's economy. | |
| c. The Chinese will be known as great inventors. | |

2. **Read the first paragraph under the heading "The Birth of a New Economy" on page 204. Then look at the blue headings on pages 204–206 and the map on page 205. What do you predict will be the result of new roads and waterways?**

_____

_____

**Name two clues from the headings and the map that helped you make your prediction.**

_____

_____

Summary also on
Audiotape

# Lesson 2 Summary
## The Flowering of Chinese Culture

(*Across the Centuries* pp. 202–208)

**Thinking Focus:** What were the most significant achievements of the Tang and Song dynasties?

## The Civil Service System

In 618, a rebellious lord named Li Yuan seized power from the Sui emperor. Li Yuan started the Tang dynasty, which was followed by the Song dynasty. Under the Tang and Song dynasties, the Chinese attained new heights in painting, poetry, education, and science.

Rulers under the Tang and Song dynasties established fair systems of government. Sui and early Tang rulers had used examinations to find good candidates for public office. But only an **aristocrat** could afford to attend special schools to study for the exam. Under later Tang and Song rulers, government workers came from other classes. Promotions for government workers under the Tang and Song were based on merit, or doing a good job. The Chinese developed the first **meritocracy,** in which government workers were promoted for doing their work well.

The Chinese believed that the emperor ruled under a **mandate,** or order, from heaven. This meant that the emperor had total power. But in reality, most emperors shared their power with aristocrats. In the new meritocracy, aristocrats had less power. Aristocrats held fewer government positions and risked losing their jobs if they did not perform well.

[?] Why did the aristocracy find it more difficult to gain influence under the civil service system?

**aristocrat**
(ə-rĭs′tə-krăt′)

a member of a privileged class having inherited wealth and high social position

**meritocracy**
(mĕr′ĭ-tŏk′rə-sē)

a system in which people are chosen for jobs and promoted based on their work

**mandate**
(măn′dāt′)

a command or instruction from an authority; an order to govern

*Summary continues on next page*

## The Birth of a New Economy

To improve travel, trade, and communication, Tang and Song rulers built new roads and waterways. These rulers also encouraged the use of new crops and farming methods. This caused a boom in agriculture that led to a population increase in southern China. The agriculture boom also meant that farmers produced a surplus. They sold this extra food to other regions, using the new roads and waterways to send their crops to market.

Merchants also used China's waterways to transport their goods. At first, people used bartered goods, such as silk, in trade. Later, merchants made copper coins with holes in the middle and strung them on a *cash,* or string. But *cash* was heavy. So the Song government began to print paper money. This money became the world's first paper **currency**. China soon developed a **money economy**, in which cash and paper currency were exchanged for goods.

**?** What factors led to a money economy in China?

## A Continuing Heritage

The Chinese continued to value their ancient traditions. More people than ever read Confucian classics. But at the same time, the Chinese improved life with new inventions.

Of all the inventions made during the Tang and Song periods, printing was the most important. Woodblock printing was invented in the late 700s. It was very time-consuming. Then in 1045, a Chinese commoner named Pi Sheng invented a much faster way of printing using movable type. Many books on law, medicine, mathematics, and science were printed. New ideas about medicine and farming spread quickly throughout China through the printed word.

In the 600s, the Chinese invented gunpowder. By 1288, they had invented guns. Chinese astronomers had begun mapping the stars by 300 B.C. During the Song dynasty, they invented a magnetic compass. Europeans later copied many of these inventions.

**?** Find evidence to support this statement: Chinese inventions showed a respect for the past as well as a desire to improve on it.

**currency**
(kûr´ən-sē)

any form of money being used as a medium of exchange

**money economy**
(mŭn´ē ĭ-kŏn´əmē)

an economy in which money is exchanged for goods

CHAPTER 8

# Lesson 3 Preview
## China and the Larger World

(*Across the Centuries* pp. 209–215)

### China and the World

|  | Yuan | Ming | Qing |
|---|---|---|---|
| **Relations with West** | International trade prospers | Overseas trade restricted | Overseas trade allowed at Guangzhou |
| **Population** | Many die in the North | New foods introduced | Population grows, territory added |

1. **Look at the graphic organizer above. Then read the following sentences and fill in the blanks.**

   a. Under the _____ Dynasty, _____ trade was restricted.

   b. Many people died in the North during the _____ Dynasty.

   c. The _____ Dynasty saw the growth of its population and territories.

2. **Look at the pictures on pages 212 and 215 in your text and read the captions. In which picture do you think the dynasty was more open to the outside world? Explain your answer.**

   _____

   _____

   _____

   _____

   _____

   _____

CHAPTER 8
# Lesson 3 Reading Strategy
## China and the Larger World

(*Across the Centuries* pp. 209–215)

**Summarize** This reading strategy helps you remember key points about what you have read. When you get to a good break in your reading, stop and write down the main ideas of what you have read.

1. Read the section "The Mongols in China" on pages 210–211. What is the best summary of what life was like under Mongol rule? Circle the letter next to the best answer.

   a. Chinese life and culture suffered, but trade increased.

   b. Kublai Khan attacked many parts of southern China.

   c. The Mongols cut off China from the rest of the world.

2. Read the section "The Ming Dynasty," on pages 211–214. What is the best summary of Ming rule? Circle the letter next to the best answer.

   a. Ming emperors restored many traditions, but they were despots who controlled every aspect of government.

   b. Ming emperors did not allow trade with other nations.

   c. Ming emperors refused to share China's knowledge with other nations.

3. Read the section "The Qing Dynasty," on pages 214–215. Then fill in the chart on life under Qing rule with a key point about each topic listed.

| Topic | Key Point |
|---|---|
| Government | |
| Population | |
| Trade with other nations | |

4. Use the key points you listed in question 3 to write a one or two sentence summary of what life was like during the Qing Dynasty.

   _____

   _____

# Lesson 3 Summary
## China and the Larger World

(*Across the Centuries* pp. 209–215)

Summary also on Audiotape

**Thinking Focus:** What factors caused China to open trade at some times and remain isolated at others?

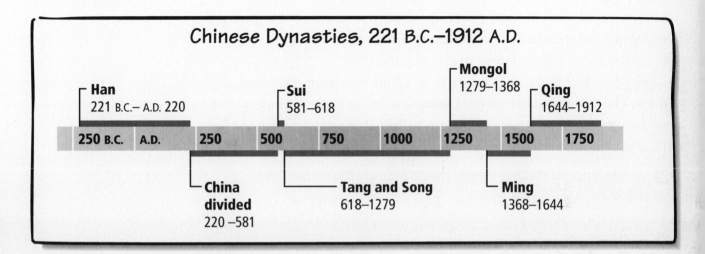

Chinese Dynasties, 221 B.C.–1912 A.D.

Han
221 B.C.– A.D. 220

Sui
581–618

Mongol
1279–1368

Qing
1644–1912

250 B.C.  A.D.  250  500  750  1000  1250  1500  1750

China divided
220 –581

Tang and Song
618–1279

Ming
1368–1644

## The Mongols in China

While southern China prospered under the Song dynasty, northern China was invaded by the Mongols from central Asia. By 1234, the Mongols ruled all of northern China. The Mongol ruler, Kublai Khan, moved his capital to Beijing and created the Yuan dynasty.

Kublai Khan adopted some Chinese traditions in order to be accepted by his subjects. But the Mongols also slowed down Chinese progress and growth. Mongols burned cities and ruined farmland. They allowed canals and irrigation systems to fall apart. Many civil servants lost their jobs because Kublai Khan gave the jobs to Mongols. But the Mongols strengthened Chinese ties to the world outside of China. Trade with western Asia thrived. Ideas such as the knowledge of printing and gunpowder probably spread from western Asia to Europe during the Mongol period.

[?] In what ways did the Mongol conquest of China affect the livelihood of most Chinese people?

*Summary continues on next page*

# The Ming Dynasty

In 1368, the Chinese rebelled against the Mongols. Their leader, Emperor Taizu, founded the Ming Dynasty, which ruled China until 1644. Taizu brought back exams for government jobs, called civil service exams. He also rebuilt irrigation systems, reservoirs, and the Great Wall. He ended slavery in China. But, like many Ming rulers, Taizu was a **despot**. He controlled all government departments. He accused thousands of people of treason and had them executed. Until the mid-1400s, the Chinese were among the best sailors in the world. But then emperors needed to spend money on stopping invasions in the north. And government officials disliked the growing importance of merchants. So the emperors stopped spending money on exploration and outlawed overseas trade.

The first European ship to arrive in China was from Portugal, in 1514. The Chinese allowed the Portuguese to set up a trading station on the coast. Later European traders had to stay at certain areas along the coast as well.

**despot**
(dĕs'pət)
a ruler who holds absolute power and uses it abusively

> **?** In what ways did the Ming dynasty affect trade and other contacts with the world?

# The Qing Dynasty

In the early 1600s, peasants from the south rebelled against strict Ming rulers and high taxes. When the Ming rulers sent their armies to the south, Manchu tribes invaded China from the north. In 1644, the Manchus created the Qing Dynasty, which lasted until 1912. Like the Mongols, the Manchus kept control of the army in their own hands. But they continued the Ming structure of government and civil service exams.

China's population grew greatly during Qing rule. In 1400, it had been 60 million. By 1850, it was about 430 million. By then, China's territory included parts of modern-day Manchuria, Mongolia, Burma, and Vietnam. Qing emperors allowed some trade. But they believed that China had little to gain by contact with the outside world.

> **?** What aspects of traditional Chinese government did the Qing retain?

# Chapter Overview
## Japan

Fill in the blank spaces below with information from the chapter.

| When: |
| --- |
| 552–1854 |
| **Where:** |
| Japan |
| **Who:** |
| The Japanese |

## Land of the Rising Sun

### The Roots of Japanese Culture

**Land:** Hokkaido, Honshu, Shikoku, _____

**Early people:** Jomon, _____

### National Culture

**Art:**
• Painting
• Carving
• Weaving

**Literature:**
• _____
• _____
• _____

### Power of the Shoguns

**Warrior Government:**
• Shogun
• Daimyo
• _____

**Religious Denominations:**
• Pure Land Buddhism
• Nichiren Buddhism
• Zen Buddhism

### Unified yet Isolated

**Class System:**
• Artisans
• Peasants
• _____

**New Culture:**
• Kabuki
• Haiku

CHAPTER 9

# Lesson 1 Preview
## Land of the Rising Sun

*(Across the Centuries* pp. 222–226)

### Early Japan

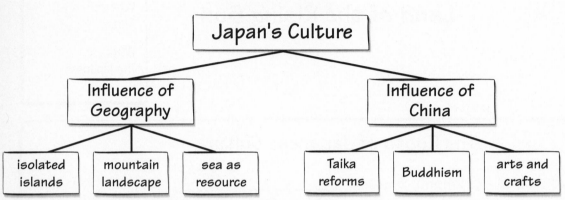

1. **Read the graphic organizer above. Use the following words to fill in the blanks below.**

   | China    isolated    Buddhism    landscape |

   a. Japan consists of several _____ islands.

   b. Japan embraced _____ as a result of influence from

      _____.

2. **Look at the map on page 224 to complete the sentence with the correct island name.**

   All of Japan's four main islands have mountains, but the tallest

   mountain, Mt. Fuji, is on _____.

CHAPTER 9

# Lesson 1 Reading Strategy
## Land of the Rising Sun

(*Across the Centuries* pp. 222–226)

**Predict/Infer** This reading strategy helps you understand what you have read and what you will read next. Before you read a section, think about the titles, pictures, and captions. Then think about what will happen in the selection.

1. **Read the first two paragraphs in the section "The Islands of Japan" on page 223. What do you predict is the result of the landscape described in the paragraphs? Circle the letter next to the best answer.**

   a. The Japanese are extremely outgoing people.

   b. The sea plays a large role in Japan's history.

   c. Japan seeks to conquer the mainland.

2. **Name one clue from your reading that helped you make your prediction.**

   _____

3. **Read the section "The Early People of Japan" on pages 224–225, and the heading that follows. What do you think will happen to Shinto as Chinese ideas influence Japan? Circle the letter next to the best answer.**

   a. Chinese ideas will have little influence on Japan.

   b. It will exist alongside Buddhism.

   c. It will replace Buddhism.

4. **Read the first five paragraphs on page 225 under "Korea and the Spread of Chinese Influence." Then fill in the chart below.**

| What I Know | What I Predict |
|---|---|
| Buddhist scholars and priests _____ | Japan _____ |
| Prince Shotoku _____ | Buddhism _____ |
| The Taika Reforms _____ | _____ |

# Lesson 1 Summary
## Land of the Rising Sun

*(Across the Centuries pp. 222–226)*

Summary also on Audiotape

---

**Thinking Focus:** How did the geography of Japan influence its development?

## The Islands of Japan

Japan includes four main islands called Hokkaido, Honshu, Shikoku, and Kyushu. It also includes many smaller islands. All the islands were formed from volcanoes millions of years ago. Japan's land area is about the size of Montana.

The nation has more than 1,500 earthquakes a year. Typhoons are also common, and heavy winds and rains batter the coasts. All of these rough conditions affect the land. Only 20 percent of the land can be used for farming. In fact, Japan has few natural resources other than the sea. The waters around Japan provide much of the nation's food. They have also protected Japan from invaders and allowed it to develop its culture in **isolation**.

**?** Why is the sea Japan's greatest natural resource?

**isolation**
(ī´sə-lā´shən)

the state of being separate from a group

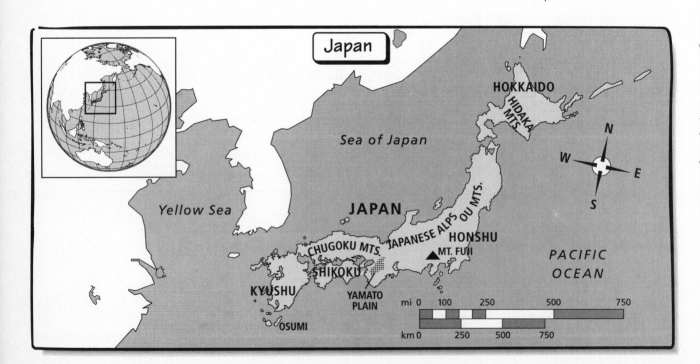

Reading Support Resources

# The Early People of Japan

Stone tools and weapons show that people who hunted animals and gathered wild plants lived in Japan over 10,000 years ago. About 8000 B.C., people of the Jomon culture appeared in Japan. Ancient fishhooks and harpoon points prove that they were fishers. Then, about 200 B.C., the Yayoi culture settled on Honshu. They grew rice in watery fields. They also used metal tools to irrigate and level the land.

Between A.D. 200 and 300, the Yayois were replaced by a "tomb culture." The tomb culture left huge graves full of mirrors, crowns, and clay statues of warriors. Sometime after 400, one ruling warrior clan became more powerful than the rest. Japan's first emperor came from this clan. His family still rules Japan today.

Early Japanese people followed the **Shinto** religion. They believed the world was filled with divine spirits, or *kami*. The emperor was thought to be a descendant of the highest kami, the Sun Goddess.

[?] How did the lifestyles of the peoples of the Jomon, Yayoi, and "tomb" cultures compare and contrast? How do we know?

> **Shinto**
> (shĭn´tŏ)
>
> a Japanese religion whose followers believe that all things in the natural world are filled with divine spirits

# Korea and the Spread of Chinese Influence

In 108 B.C., China's Han dynasty took over northwestern Korea. Five hundred years later, Buddhism spread from China into Korea. By the 660s, Korea was sending Buddhist scholars and priests to Japan.

Because Buddhism had strengthened China's government, the powerful Japanese Soga clan thought it would also strengthen Japan's government. After Prince Shotoku came to rule as regent in 593, he encouraged Buddhism and the spread of Chinese culture.

After Prince Shotoku's death, the government made changes called the Taika Reforms. All farmland outside the capital city became the property of the emperor. These Chinese-style changes weakened the power of the clan leaders and strengthened the emperor.

[?] Why did Chinese culture spread throughout Japan?

CHAPTER 9

# Lesson 2 Preview
## A Developing National Culture

(*Across the Centuries* pp. 227–230)

### Kyoto Culture

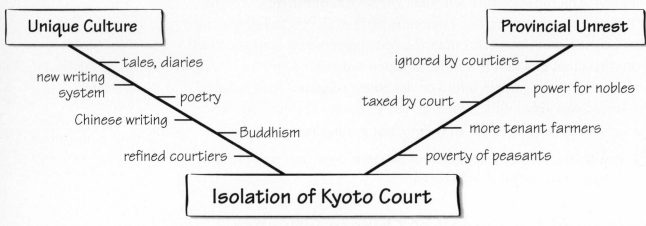

Unique Culture

tales, diaries

new writing
system

poetry

Chinese writing

Buddhism

refined courtiers

Provincial Unrest

ignored by courtiers

power for nobles

taxed by court

more tenant farmers

poverty of peasants

Isolation of Kyoto Court

1. **Look at the graphic organizer above, then check off which is the best summary of information from the graphic.**

___ **a.** The isolation of the Kyoto court limited Japan's development.

___ **b.** The isolation of the Kyoto court had cultural advantages and political disadvantages for Japan.

___ **c.** The isolation of the Kyoto court let Japan develop without limitations from the outside world.

2. **Look at the chart on page 229. Then describe two ways in which Kanji writing differs from Hiragana writing.**

_____

_____

_____

_____

_____

_____

_____

CHAPTER 9

# Lesson 2 Reading Strategy
## A Developing National Culture

(*Across the Centuries* pp. 227–230)

**Cause and Effect** This reading strategy helps you understand events and why they occur. As you read, think about the factors that caused an event. Then think about what the effects of that event may be.

1. Read the section "A Court of Refinement" on pages 227–228. Which of the following sentences describes the effects of moving the capital to Kyoto? Circle the letter next to the best answer.

   a. The capital became isolated from events in the provinces.

   b. The court lived in poverty and fear.

   c. The power of Buddhist monks increased.

2. Read the section "The Literature of the Court" on pages 228–229. What was one effect of the writing styles that developed in Japan?

   _____

   _____

3. Read page 230. Which sentence best describes why farmers became poor? Circle the letter next to the best answer.

   a. They were isolated from life at court.

   b. They were taxed by the government and the courtiers.

   c. The Taika Reforms broke up their lands.

4. Identify the following events in the cause-effect chain as causes or effects. Write a *C* if the event is a cause; write an *E* if the event is an effect.

   a. ___ The imperial government ignored life in the provinces.

   b. ___ Small landowners gave up their land to nobles.

   c. ___ Provincial nobles take over much land.

# Lesson 2 Summary
## A Developing National Culture

*(Across the Centuries* pp. 227–230)

**Thinking Focus:** How did moving the capital to Kyoto affect the development of Japanese culture?

## A Court of Refinement

In 794, the government of Japan moved its capital to Kyoto. In the new capital, the emperor limited the number of Buddhist temples and monasteries that could be built. He wanted to keep the clergy out of politics.

The Fujiwara clan became powerful in Kyoto by marrying into the imperial family. Fujiwara women married princes. Fujiwara men served as **regents** for the emperor. Between 858 and 1185, Fujiwara men often ruled for the emperor.

Japanese culture flourished at the court in Kyoto. **Courtiers** developed fine manners and a sense of delicacy, or good taste for the arts. Japanese literature and customs developed from the language and traditions that the courtiers brought from China. Courtiers followed Shingon Buddhism, which stressed ceremony, ritual, learning, and art.

? What were some of the activities of the courtiers at Kyoto?

**regent**
(rē´jənt)
person who rules for a monarch

**courtier**
(kôr´tē-ər)
person who takes part in the refined social life of a court

## The Literature of the Court

Poetry was the favorite form of literature of the court. Courtiers composed short poems for every occasion, and poetry contests were popular. The courtiers admired beauty in nature. Some of their literature expressed a sentimental sadness at the passing beauty of natural things. They called this sadness *aware (ah wah RAY).*

*Summary continues on next page*

Japan borrowed its writing system from China. But Japanese writers also developed characters called *hiragana* to represent syllables rather than words. Women, who were not expected to learn Chinese, used hiragana to write some of the greatest literature of the age. The diary of Lady Murasaki Shikibu told much about the life of women of the court. Lady Murasaki also wrote what is possibly the world's first novel, called *Tale of Genji*. It was the crowning literary achievement of its time.

## Writing Styles of Japan

| Style | Words (shinto) | (haiku) | Description | Origin |
|---|---|---|---|---|
| Kanji | 神道 | 俳句 | Pictograms of concepts | Writing system adopted from Chinese characters |
| Hiragana | しんとう | はいく | Phonetic symbols of one syllable each | Writing system originated and simplified in Japan |

**?** What kinds of literature developed at the court of Kyoto?

# Life in the Provinces

Courtiers lived a life of luxury because they owned land in the provinces. They collected taxes from the farmers who worked on their estates. That meant the farmers were taxed twice—once by the government and once by the landowners. To avoid paying taxes, many farmers gave up their land to nobles. They became tenant farmers who had to pay rent in order to farm small plots of land. Others became laborers on great estates. Most were very poor. They worked all day and slept in small huts at night. Compared to them, the courtiers seemed like "dwellers in the clouds." Indeed, the courtiers weren't concerned about the poor. They looked down on peasant farmers and laborers.

**?** How did life in the Japanese provinces differ from life at the Kyoto court?

CHAPTER 9
# Lesson 3 Preview
## The Power of the Shoguns
(*Across the Centuries* pp. 231–236)

### The Rise of the Shoguns

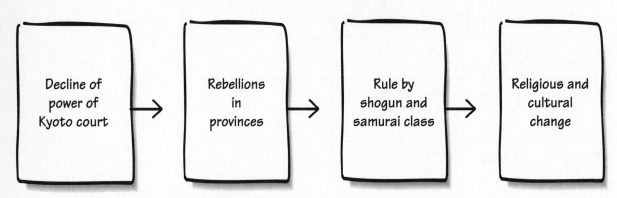

Decline of power of Kyoto court → Rebellions in provinces → Rule by shogun and samurai class → Religious and cultural change

1. **Study the graphic organizer above, then read the following list of events. Place the events in order according to which happened first, second, third, and fourth.**

   ____ Power of Kyoto court declines

   ____ Power of shoguns rises

   ____ Cultural changes take place

   ____ People rebel

2. **Look at the picture of a samurai on page 233. Find at least one additional picture that shows how a samurai was expected to behave. Based on what you have seen in the pictures, list three qualities a samurai should have.**

   _____

   _____

   _____

   _____

   _____

   _____

   _____

   _____

CHAPTER 9

# Lesson 3 Reading Strategy
## The Power of the Shoguns

(*Across the Centuries* pp. 231–236)

**Summarize** This reading strategy helps you to remember the key points about what you have read. When you get to a good break in your reading, stop and write down the main ideas of what you have read.

1. **Read from the top of page 232 to the heading "Development of Religious Denominations" on page 234. Circle the letter next to the best summary of a warrior government.**

   a. The shogun and his samurai served the daimyo. The daimyo supported them in return for their protection and service.

   b. Warrior clans served the shogun. They fought rebellious nobles and monks.

   c. The shogun replaced the emperor. The daimyo and and their samurai served him.

**Use the section "A Warrior Government" on pages 232–234 to answer questions 2 and 3.**

2. **Fill in the chart below to summarize a warrior government.**

<u>What I Learned</u>

_____

_____

_____

_____

3. **Write a short summary of how the Ashikaga shogunate came to power.**

   _____

   _____

   _____

# Lesson 3 Summary
## The Power of the Shoguns

(*Across the Centuries* pp. 231–236)

Summary also on Audiotape

**Thinking Focus:** What impact did samurai values have on Japanese culture and religion?

## A Warrior Government

The Kyoto court ignored the provinces for too long. Nobles and Buddhist monks in the provinces began to rebel. Warrior clans came to the rescue. By 1185, the Minamoto had set up a warrior government. Japan's medieval era had begun.

In 1192, the emperor gave Yoritomo, the leader of the Minamoto clan, the title of **shogun**, or great general. Yoritomo made his headquarters at Kamakura. The **daimyo**, or noble estate lords, supported him. Warriors who protected the daimyos' estates were called **samurai**.

In the late 1200s, samurai protected Japan from an attack by the Mongols. When the government could not reward them, the samurai burned Kamakura to the ground. After many battles, the Ashikaga family formed a new shogunate and took over Japan. They ruled from Kyoto and adopted courtier ways. The Ashikaga shogunate lasted until the late 1500s.

**?** How were the warrior governments organized?

## Development of Religious Denominations

During medieval times, Buddhism changed to meet the needs of the Japanese people. Different forms, or **denominations**, of Buddhism developed. For example, Pure Land Buddhists chanted the name of Amida Buddha, an ancient spiritual Buddha. Pure Land Buddhists hoped to find happiness in an afterlife.

In the 1200s, the monk Nichiren founded another Buddhist denomination. Nichiren Buddhism taught that truth was only in the Lotus Sutra. The Lotus Sutra was believed to be the Buddha's last teaching.

**shogun**
(shō´gən)
a military leader who ruled Japan

**daimyo**
(dīm´yō)
the lord of an estate, who supported the shogun in feudal Japan

**samurai**
(săm´ər-rī´)
a knight in feudal Japan, from the term meaning "those who serve"

**denomination**
(dĭ-nŏm´ə-nā´shən)
an organized religious group

*Summary continues on next page*

The Zen Buddhist denomination did physical and mental exercises. Members hoped to reach sudden enlightenment, or understanding of the world, through these exercises. Zen became popular with many samurai because it stressed discipline. Some Zen masters also scoffed at book learning, logic, and other mental skills. This pleased many samurai warriors who could not read.

## Denominations of Buddhism

| Pure Land Buddhists | Nichiren Buddhists | Zen Buddhists |
|---|---|---|
| • chanted name of Amida Buddha<br><br>• hoped to find happiness in afterlife | • believed Lotus Sutra to be Buddha's last teaching<br><br>• believed truth is only in Lotus Sutra | • practiced physical and mental exercises in order to reach sudden enlightenment<br><br>• stressed discipline |

[?] How was Japanese society affected by Zen Buddhism?

## A Unified Culture

Buddhism affected the culture of medieval Japan. For example, Zen monks developed the Japanese tea ceremony so that every stage would be meaningful. Buddhist values also can be seen in Japanese Noh drama, which stresses gestures and dance steps.

Buddhism taught that humans are a part of nature. This idea was reflected in Japanese gardens, which included simple, natural forms. The gardens provided a calm, quiet place in which people could meditate, or focus on their thoughts. Flower arranging, incense blending, and painting were also influenced by Zen Buddhism.

[?] What new art forms developed in medieval Japan?

CHAPTER 9

# Lesson 4 Preview
## Japan: Unified Yet Isolated

(*Across the Centuries* pp. 237–242)

## Medieval Japan

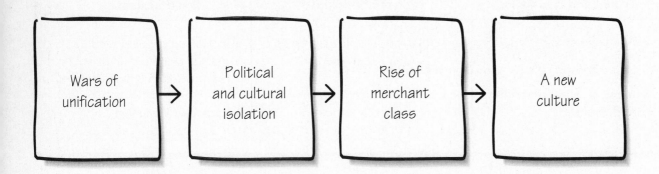

1. **Look at the graphic organizer above. Then read the following list of events. Place the events in order according to which happened first, second, third, and fourth.**

   ___ The merchant class becomes prominent.

   ___ A new culture forms.

   ___ Japan undergoes political and cultural isolation.

   ___ Wars end in unification.

2. **Read the lesson title and the red and blue headings in your text on pages 237–241. Use words from those headings to fill in the lesson outline below.**

   Japan: Unified Yet Isolated

      **I.** An _____ Shogunate

        **A.** Wars of _____

        **B.** The Tokugawa _____

        **C.** _____ in Japan

     **II.** Control of the _____

    **III.** A New and Different _____

CHAPTER 9

# Lesson 4 Reading Strategy
## Japan: Unified Yet Isolated

(*Across the Centuries* pp. 237–242)

**Sequence** This reading strategy helps you follow the order of events. As you read, pay attention to dates and times, as well as to words such as *before*, *finally*, *after*, and *then*.

1. Read the section "An All-Powerful Shogunate" on pages 238–239. List the words and phrases that help you follow the sequence of events leading to the establishment of the Tokugawa shogunate.

   _____

2. According to the text, what were two of the events that led to the Tokugawa shogunate? Put them in proper sequence.

   _____

   _____

3. Read the section "Control of the Classes" on page 240. Then number the following events in the correct sequence.

   ____ Merchants set prices and charged interest.

   ____ Merchants became rich.

   ____ Trade expanded to other cities.

   ____ Merchants suffered many restrictions.

   ____ Merchants adopted the use of money.

   ____ Wealthy merchants' power grew.

4. Read the section "A New and Different Culture" on pages 240–241. Identify the steps by which the merchant class helped create a new culture.

   a. _____

   b. _____

   c. _____

   d. _____

# Lesson 4 Summary
## Japan: Unified Yet Isolated

*(Across the Centuries* pp. 237–242)

**Thinking Focus:** Why did the Tokugawa shoguns want to keep Japan isolated?

## An All-Powerful Shogunate

During the late medieval period, one leader after another tried to gain control of Japan. In 1600, Tokugawa Ieyasu took power. To unify Japan, he established his shogunate in Edo, now called Tokyo, and set up a line of **succession**, much like a monarchy. The Tokugawa shogunate lasted for more than 250 years. Ieyasu required daimyo to swear an oath of loyalty, give military aid to the shogun, and work regularly in Edo.

The shoguns wanted to avoid the religious wars they saw in Europe. They also feared that if the daimyo became rich from foreign trade, they might rebel. So the shogunate outlawed Christianity, restricted travel, and banned European trade. Japan set a course of isolation from the influences of the West.

[?] What steps did the Tokugawa shoguns take to unify Japan?

**succession**
(sək-sĕsh´ən)
the order in which one person after another gets a title, throne, or estate

## Control of the Classes

The shogunate enforced a strict social system with four classes. The samurai warriors were the highest class. Then, in order came the artisans, peasants, and merchants.

By trading in Edo and other cities, the merchants prospered. By 1600, they traded with gold and silver coins instead of rice. By 1700, they had formed a money-based economy. Merchants got rich and became powerful by setting prices and charging interest on loans.

[?] How did Japan's economy change during the Tokugawa era?

*Summary continues on next page*

## A New and Different Culture

In the late 1600s, the merchants spent their money on new forms of entertainment. Cities had pleasure quarters with theaters, teahouses, gambling houses, wrestling, and public baths. Some of the new cultural forms were long lasting. For example, wandering ballad singers and dancers acted out romances and samurai tales. These developed into Kabuki theater, still practiced today.

Epic novels also became popular during this time. So did **haiku**, a short three-line poem that creates a mood or brings about a sudden insight. During the 1500s and 1600s, education spread to all social classes and the economy boomed.

> **haiku**
> (hī´kōō)
> three-line poem consisting of 17 syllables

[?] What role did the new merchant class play in the development of a new popular culture?

## Southeast Asia

Southeast Asia includes what are now Burma, Thailand, Laos, Cambodia, Vietnam, Malaysia, Singapore, Indonesia, Brunei, and the Philippines. In the first thousand years A.D., Southeast Asia was greatly influenced by Chinese politics and Indian religious thought. China ruled Vietnam as a province from about 100 B.C. to A.D. 900. China wanted Vietnamese sailors to export its silk and spices. Vietnamese sailors traveled to Indonesia with the goods. Then Indonesians took the goods to Malaya. From there, Indian ships took the goods further west.

Islam first came to Southeast Asia in the 1290s. It spread throughout Southeast Asia. Some wealthy Muslim leaders formed Muslim states. The richest was Malacca on the west coast of Malaya. In the 1500s Malacca became the center of trade for Southeast Asia. Traders began coming to Southeast Asia for cotton, silk, pepper, cloves, perfumes, and dyes.

[?] How did outside influences from China, India, and the rest of the world affect Southeast Asian civilizations?

# Chapter Overview
## Feudal Europe and Japan

**Fill in the blank spaces below with information from the chapter.**

### Feudal Europe and Japan, 476–1854

#### Early Medieval Europe

**Clovis's achievements:** Expanded Frankish territory; led Franks into Christianity

**Charlemagne's achievements:** _____

_____

#### Daily Life in Feudal Europe

**Life in the Country:** _____

_____

**Life in the Town:** Trade, guilds, merchants, money lending

#### Feudal Europe and Feudal Japan

**Similarities:** Codes of honor, warring clans, ___•_____

**Differences:** Feudalism ends in Europe, lasts in Japan

CHAPTER 10

# Lesson 1 Preview
## Europe After the Roman Empire

*(Across the Centuries pp. 256–261)*

### Europe After the Romans

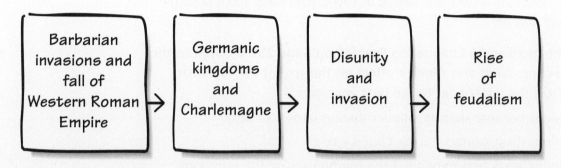

1. **Look at the graphic organizer above. Then read the following sentences and fill in the blanks.**

   a. The _____ invaded the Western Roman Empire.

   b. Name one thing that happened after the fall of the Western Roman Empire.

   _____

2. **Look at the map on page 257. What major empire is shown in the southeastern corner of the map?**

   _____

CHAPTER 10

# Lesson 1 Reading Strategy
## Europe After the Roman Empire

(*Across the Centuries* pp. 256–261)

**Cause and Effect** This reading strategy helps you understand events and why they occur. As you read, think about the factors that caused an event. Then think about what the effects of that event may be.

1. **Read from the heading "A Conquering People" on page 257 through to the end of the section. What was Clovis's effect on the size of the Frankish kingdom? Circle the letter next to the best answer.**

   **a.** The kingdom became slightly smaller during Clovis's reign.

   **b.** The kingdom disappeared during Clovis's reign.

   **c.** Clovis fought wars that expanded the boundaries or the kingdom.

2. **Read from the blue heading "An Age of Learning" on page 258 to the blue heading "Jews in Medieval Europe" on page 259. What was the main cause of the fall of Charlemagne's empire? Circle the letter next to the best answer.**

   **a.** Charlemagne spent too much money on educating his people.

   **b.** Charlemagne became very ill.

   **c.** Enemies kept attacking the empire from all sides.

3. **Read from the blue heading "Europe After Charlemagne" on page 259 to the end of the section on page 260. What were some of the effects of Charlemagne's death?**

   _____

   _____

4. **Read the section "Medieval England" on pages 260–261. Then fill in the chart**

| Cause | Effect |
|---|---|
| a. King Edward dies childless. | |
| b. | Feudalism begins in England. |
| c. King gives land to vassals. | |

# Lesson 1 Summary
## Europe After the Roman Empire

(*Across the Centuries* pp. 256–261)

**Thinking Focus:** What conditions after the fall of Rome led to the rise of feudalism?

## Rise of the Germanic Kingdoms

The fall of the Roman Empire began a period known as the Middle Ages. During this time, Europe changed.

- Germanic rulers, who led groups known as barbarians, divided up the lands of Europe.
- The Franks, led by King Clovis, formed a strong bond with the Christian Church.
- Monks formed **monasteries** where they held church writings and kept alive some Roman and Greek ideas.
- Most of Europe stayed Christian after Charles Martel defeated the Muslims at Tours, France, in 732.

**?** What important changes took place in Europe after the fall of Rome?

> **monastery**
> (mŏn′ə-stĕr′ē)
> a place where a group of religious people live

Barbarian Kingdoms

Norse
Swedes
Finns
North Sea
Danes
Baltic Sea
Angles
Saxons
Jutes
Frisians
Balts
Slavs
Celts
Saxons
Thuringians
Bavarians
Franks
Lombards
Bretons
Burgundians
Ostrogoths
Gepids
ATLANTIC OCEAN
Basques
Suevi
BYZANTINE
Black Sea
Visigoths
Vandals
EMPIRE
MEDITERRANEAN SEA
mi 0 300 600

## Charlemagne's Empire

Charlemagne, one of the kings of the Franks, became more than just a king. In 800, the pope crowned him emperor of what had once been the Western Roman Empire. His 48-year rule was taken up with war. Everyone who lost to Charlemagne in battle had to swear loyalty to him and become Christian. Charlemagne wanted to strengthen the church. He forced church leaders to learn to read and tried to get rid of bad people in the church. He made sure that Christian church services were performed the same way throughout Europe. At the same time, he tolerated other religions. Jewish culture was strong in the countries that are now France and Germany.

Charlemagne put great value on learning. Though many books had been destroyed during the wars, he had scholars copy books by hand so that they would be preserved for the future.

**[?]** How did Charlemagne improve learning and the quality of the church in medieval Europe?

## Medieval England

During the 800s, England was attacked again and again by a people called the Vikings. But the English king, Alfred the Great, was strong. He fought the Vikings for 30 years. Many years after Alfred's death, William, the Duke of Normandy in France, said that he was the real ruler of England. William and his army invaded and defeated English forces in 1066. William became known as King William the Conqueror. William used an arrangement called **feudalism** to set up his kingdom. King William gave large pieces of land, or **fiefs**, to the soldiers who had fought for him. The new landowners became his **vassals**. Each of them swore an **oath of fealty** to the king. If the king needed help, his vassals sent their **knights** to do battle. A **hierarchy** developed between these different groups of people. This means that there were different ranks, or levels, of authority and power. All of these groups in the feudal society had to be loyal to the king.

**[?]** Describe the condition of Europe after Charlemagne's death.

**feudalism**
(fyōōd′l-ĭz′əm)

a political and economic arrangement in which a lord provides protection in exchange for loyalty and service

**fief**
(fēf)

a large feudal estate

**vassal**
(văs′əl)

a person under the protection of a feudal lord

**oath of fealty**
(ōth ŭv fē′əl-tē)

a statement of loyalty

**knight**
(nīt)

an armed soldier who fights on horseback

**hierarchy**
(hī′ə-rär′kē)

a group of people organized by rank or power

## CHAPTER 10
# Lesson 2 Preview
## Daily Life in Feudal Europe

*(Across the Centuries pp. 262–270)*

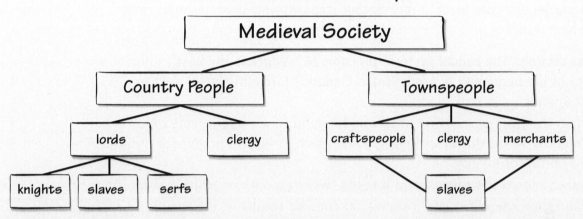

Life in Medieval Europe

1. **Look at the graphic organizer above. Then read the following sentences and fill in the blanks.**

   a.  The two groups that made up European medieval society were

   _____ and _____.

   b.  _____, _____, _____, and

   _____ were four groups of people who lived in
   medieval towns.

2. **Look at the chart "Becoming a Medieval Knight" on page 265. Then fill in the blanks in the following paragraph:**

   The first step for a boy to become a knight was to be a _____.

   Then at the age of _____ to _____, the boy

   became a _____. Then, between the ages of _____

   and _____, he became a knight. This job included serving his

   lord as a warrior, overseeing his land as a vassal, and taking part in

   _____.

CHAPTER 10

# Lesson 2 Reading Strategy
## Daily Life in Feudal Europe

(*Across the Centuries* pp. 262–270)

**Summarize** This reading strategy helps you remember key points about what you have read. When you get to a good break in your reading, stop and write down the main ideas of what you have read.

1. **Read the section "The Feudal System" on page 263. Which is the best summary of the beginning of feudalism in England? Circle the letter next to the best answer.**

   a. William the Conqueror wanted to rule England much like he ruled in Normandy. To do this he established feudalism, a way of governing based on ties of loyalty.

   b. Vassals honored their lords, and knights swore an oath of fealty.

   c. William the Conqueror had a survey taken. The results of the survey were published in a book.

2. **Read from the blue heading "Clergy" on page 268 through the end of the section. Summarize the lives of the monks and nuns who lived in monasteries.**

   _____

   _____

3. **Read the section called "Guilds" on page 269. Summarize the guild system that was practiced in medieval towns.**

   _____

   _____

4. **Read the section "The Forces of Change" on page 270. Fill in the chart below with summaries of the information in each column head.**

   | King John's Reign | The Magna Carta |
   |---|---|
   |  |  |
   |  |  |

# Lesson 2 Summary
## Daily Life in Feudal Europe

(*Across the Centuries* pp. 262–270)

---

**Thinking Focus:** How did the feudal system affect the everyday lives of people in Europe?

---

## The Feudal System

William the Conqueror used the feudal system as a means of peacefully ruling his kingdom. The king's vassals (subjects) paid **homage,** or showed honor to the king. An oath of fealty, or loyalty, was sworn between the king and a lord, or between a lord and a knight. In return, the king gave his lords fiefs, or large pieces of land.

**?** Why was loyalty important in the feudal system?

## Life in the Country

The lord of each fief lived in a castle. The castle and all its lands were known as a **manor.** A fief might be divided into a number of manors. The castle was the center of feudal life. Knights living at the castle received food, housing, and a horse. In exchange, they protected the manor in times of war. When the men were at war, women took over the running of the manor. A few noblewomen controlled fiefs or convents.

The peasants on the manor had very humble homes. Their animals lived under the same roof. **Serfs** were peasants who were bound to the land they farmed for their feudal lord. Unlike slaves, who could be sold or given away, serfs had to work on a piece of land no matter who owned it.

Religion was an important part of medieval life. Most manors had a small church on them. Some clergy lived in monasteries. There they studied and copied old books by hand, took care of the sick, ran schools, and did other good works.

**?** How did each class help to keep a feudal manor running?

**homage**
(hŏm′ĭj)
an act of honor or respect

**manor**
(măn′ər)
a castle and estate of a lord

**serf**
(sûrf)
a member of the lowest feudal class, bound to the land and owned by a lord

*Summary continues on next page*

# Life in the Town

After the fall of the Western Roman Empire, there were few towns in Europe. But in the 1000s town life began once again. Trade became important. Craftspeople formed **guilds** to control their trades. For example, this meant that all weavers belonged to a special weavers union. Guilds put a limit on how many people could set up business. Only experts at their trade could join a guild. Jews were not allowed to join guilds and many became merchants.

During this time, some women were merchants.. They produced goods in their homes, such as cloth. If a woman's husband was a guild member, she, too, might become a member. Some women in France formed all-female guilds.

**guild**
(gĭld)

an organized group of skilled tradespeople

**?** Describe the new social order that evolved in medieval towns.

# The Forces of Change

By the time King John came to power in 1199, the feudal lords were very powerful. King John led England into many losing wars. He asked for higher and higher taxes. This angered the vassals who lost fiefs in northern France. Many lords turned against King John. In 1215, they forced him to sign the *Magna Carta*. This document accepts the rights of the nobles. It stopped the king from taking those rights away. By accepting the power of the lords, the *Magna Carta* led the way to rule by law rather than rule by monarchs.

**?** How did the *Magna Carta* pave the way for a new social system in England?

**CHAPTER 10**

# Lesson 3 Preview
## Two Feudal Societies

(*Across the Centuries* pp. 271–274)

### Feudal Europe and Japan

|  | Knight | Samurai |
|---|---|---|
| **Society** | feudal Europe | feudal Japan |
| **Style of Battle** | horseback; lances | swords, arrows |
| **Code of honor** | chivalry | bushido |
| **Period of Importance** | 800s-1300s | 1100s-1800s |

1. **Look at the graphic organizer above. Then read the following sentences and fill in the blanks.**

   a. Both the European knight and the Japanese samurai lived in

   _____ societies.

   b. Which group's period of importance was the longest?

   _____

2. **Look at the two pictures on page 271. Name one way the European knight is similar to the Japanese samurai. Then name one way the two are different.**

   Alike: _____

   _____

   _____

   Different: _____

   _____

   _____

CHAPTER 10

# Lesson 3 Reading Strategy
## Two Feudal Societies

(*Across the Centuries* pp. 271–274)

**Compare and Contrast** This reading strategy helps you understand how events are similar and different. As you read about historical events, think about how they compare and contrast with events you already know.

1. Read from the heading "Similar Societies" on page 272 to the blue heading "Codes of Honor" on page 273. Then fill in the chart below with information that compares and contrasts the warrior knights of England and the Japanese samurai.

| | Similar | Different |
|---|---|---|
| a. Place in society | | |
| b. Style of battle | | |

2. Read from the blue heading "Codes of Honor" on page 273 to the end of the page. Write two sentences about the similarities between chivalry and bushido.

   _____

   _____

3. Write two sentences contrasting chivalry and bushido.

   _____

   _____

4. Read the section "Different Societies" on page 274. Write two sentences comparing and contrasting European feudalism with Japanese feudalism.

   _____

   _____

# Lesson 3 Summary
## Two Feudal Societies

*(Across the Centuries* pp. 271–274)

**Thinking Focus:** In what ways were feudal Japan and feudal Europe alike and different?

## Similar Societies

Like England, Japan had a form of feudalism. English lords used warrior knights to protect their manors. These knights were an important part of the feudal society. Japanese lords used warriors called *samurai* to protect their estates. In the 1100s, the samurai became a new class in Japanese society. European knights mostly went into battle on horseback. They used long spears. The Japanese samurai warriors sometimes fought on horseback. But often they fought on foot. They used weapons such as swords, and bows and arrows. English knights lived by a system of honor called **chivalry**. They were expected to be kind, brave, and loyal to their lords. They were also expected to defend people who could not defend themselves. The samurai had a similar system. It was called **bushido**. Samurai warriors were willing to give up their lives for their lords. Part of the samurai code was to set a good example. Samurai felt it was their duty to show the lower classes the right way to live. Both systems gave security to people at all levels of society.

**?** How did the system of feudalism meet the needs of both medieval Europe and Japan?

**chivalry**
(shĭv′əl-rē)

a code of conduct for English knights in the Middle Ages that called for honor, loyalty, and fairness

**bushido**
(bōōsh′ĭ-dō′)

a code of conduct for Japanese samurai warriors that called for loyalty and honor

*Summary continues on next page*

## Feudalism in Japan and Europe

| Feudal England | Feudal Japan |
|---|---|
| System exists until the 1400s | System exists until the mid-1800s |
| Knights protect lords and manors | Samurai protect lords' estates |
| Chivalry is practiced | Bushido is practiced |

# Different Societies

Japanese feudalism lasted until the mid-1800s. In Europe, feudalism ended 400 years earlier. The growth of towns weakened the feudal system in Europe. People left the feudal system behind when they settled in towns. Also, new weapons, such as guns, made it hard for knights to fight on horseback. Most became more interested in watching over their land than in fighting. Some knights wouldn't fight even when they were called to military service.

Japanese feudalism lasted longer than English feudalism because the samurai who were not warriors took jobs with the government. Also, from 1635 to 1854, Japan sealed itself off from the West so the Japanese did not learn about guns until 1854. But after 1854, Japanese feudalism quickly declined.

**[?]**   Why did feudalism last so much longer in Japan than it did in Europe?

# Chapter Overview
## Europe: Rule, Religion, and Conflict

**Fill in the blanks with information from the chapter.**

| When: |
| 726–1204 |
| **Where:** |
| Europe, Byzantine Empire, Middle East |
| **Who:** |
| Christians, Muslims, and Jews |

## Europe in the Middle Ages

### The Church in Western Europe

**Power of the Church:**
hierarchy, popes, _____
_____

**Struggles with Kings:**
Gregory VII vs. King _____

**The Church and Daily Life:**
The Age of _____

### The Church in the East

**Capital City:**
_____

**Eastern Christianity:**
• Hagia _____
• The Bishop of Constantinople is
  called _____

**Enemies:**
• Persians
• Muslim Arabs
• _____

### Crusade for the Holy Land

**Effects on the West:** _____
_____
_____

CHAPTER 11
# Lesson 1 Preview
## The Power of the Church
(*Across the Centuries* pp. 282–288)

### The Christian Church in Europe

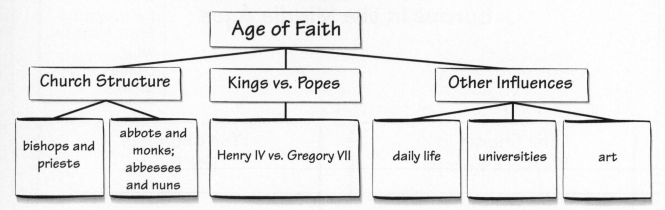

1. **Look at the graphic organizer above. Then read the following sentences and fill in the blanks.**

   a. Monks, abbots, abbesses, and nuns are part of the _____.

   b. Henry IV and Gregory VII were a _____ and a

      _____.

2. **Look through the pictures in this lesson and read the captions. What do the pictures tell you about the church in western Europe?**

   _____

   _____

   _____

   _____

CHAPTER 11

# Lesson 1 Reading Strategy
## The Power of the Church

(*Across the Centuries* pp. 282–288)

**Predict/Infer** This reading strategy helps you understand what you have read and what you will read next. Before you read a section, think about the titles, pictures, and captions. Then think about what will happen in the selection.

1. **Read the heading "A Powerful Church in Europe" and the two blue headings "The Church Hierarchy" and "The Church's Influence" on page 283. What can you infer, or conclude, from reading these headings? Circle the letter next to the best answer.**

   a. The church was a central part of life for Europeans.

   b. The pope is the most powerful member of the clergy.

   c. Most people in Europe in the 800s did not go to church.

2. **Name two clues from the headings that helped you make your inference.**

   _____

   _____

3. **Now read the section "A Powerful Church in Europe" on pages 283–284. Based on what happened between Louis VI and Abbot Suger, what do you predict will happen next? Circle the letter next to the best answer.**

   a. Popes will be crowned kings.

   b. There will be conflicts between the church and political leaders.

   c. The people of Europe will give up going to church.

4. **Now read the section heading "A Power Struggle Between Kings and Popes" and the three blue headings that follow it on pages 284–285. Who do you predict will take part in the power struggle?**

   _____

   _____

5. **Now read the section "A Power Struggle Between Kings and Popes" on pages 284–285 up to the blue heading "The Treaty." Then fill in the chart below.**

| What I know: | What I predict about the treaty: |
|---|---|
|  |  |
|  |  |

# Lesson 1 Summary
## The Power of the Church

*(Across the Centuries* pp. 282–288)

**Thinking Focus:** What aspects of European society did the church dominate from 1100 to 1300?

## A Powerful Church in Europe

Between 800 and 1300, almost all the people of Europe were Christians. The Christian church was organized in a hierarchy so that each member of the **clergy** had a rank and duties within the church. Priests led local churches called parishes. A group of parishes together made up a diocese, which was led by a bishop. The dioceses were grouped into provinces, or archdioceses. The leader of an archdiocese was an archbishop. Cardinals had even more power. They were advisers to the pope. The head of the whole Christian church was the pope.

Women were not allowed to serve as priests, bishops, archbishops, or popes. They became nuns, or "Brides of Christ." Abbesses ran their convents, or communities. Monks lived in monasteries headed by abbots. Monks and nuns lived a life of prayer, gave up riches, and worked to help the poor. The church was the largest landowner in Europe. The clergy were often the only ones in the community who could read and write. They advised kings about all sorts of government matters. This gave the clergy political power.

**clergy**
(klûr´jē)
a group of people who perform religious services

### Roman Catholic Church Leadership

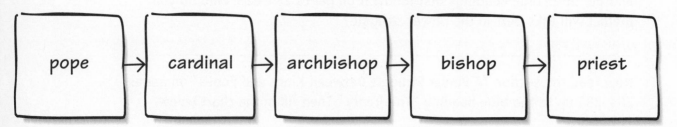

pope → cardinal → archbishop → bishop → priest

? Describe the hierarchy of the church.

*Summary continues on next page*

## A Power Struggle Between Kings and Popes

In 1073, Gregory VII became pope. He did not like the way kings were giving important church jobs to their friends. In 1075, he sent out a statement that a pope's rank was higher than a king's rank. The statement also said that kings who did not obey the pope could be removed from their thrones.

King Henry IV of Germany did not like Gregory VII's statement. He demanded that the pope give up his office. The pope's answer to this was to announce Henry IV's **excommunication**. This meant he was thrown out of the church. Henry looked for support from his nobles, but they were afraid. Finally, Henry had to give in to the pope.

**?** Why is the conflict between Henry IV and Pope Gregory significant?

## The Age of Faith

European Christians tried to live by the ideas of the church. They were looking for **salvation**. To be saved from their sins, the church said people had to accept the beliefs of the church, live good lives, and perform good works. They also paid a yearly **tithe** to the church. The church was the center of daily life and brought Christian people together. It also pushed away, and often punished, people with different beliefs, including Jews.

Until the 1100s, education took place only in monasteries. But as European towns grew, people wanted a chance to educate themselves. This desire to learn came partly from the flow of knowledge from the Muslim world. Muslims and Jews had translated books by Greek, African, and Asian writers. Groups of students and teachers who gathered in towns formed **universities**. These became popular centers of learning.

The art of this time included many paintings and sculptures of Jesus and huge cathedrals built in the Gothic style. These churches were large buildings that were meant to fill people with wonder at the power of God.

**?** How did the church influence European culture between the 1100s and 1300s?

**excommunication**
(ĕks´kə-myoo´nĭ-kā´shən)

the act that takes away someone's membership in the church

**salvation**
(săl-vā´shən)

the saving of a soul from sin

**tithe**
(tīth)

a 10th of someone's income paid to the church

**university**
(yoo´nə-vûr´sĭ-tē)

a place of higher learning

**CHAPTER 11**

# Lesson 2 Preview
## The Byzantine Empire

*(Across the Centuries* **pp. 289–294)**

### The Byzantine Empire

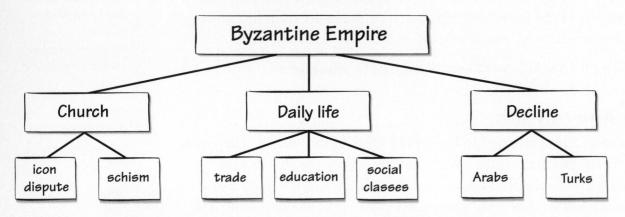

1. **Look at the graphic organizer above. Then read the following sentences and fill in the blanks.**

   a. What are two activities that contributed to the social classes in the Byzantine Empire?

   _____

   _____

   b. Which two cultures helped bring about the decline of the Byzantine Empire?

   _____

   _____

2. **Look at the map on page 290. What do you notice about the location of Constantinople?**

   _____

   _____

   _____

   _____

   _____

Reading Support Resources

CHAPTER 11

# Lesson 2 Reading Strategy
## The Byzantine Empire

*(Across the Centuries* pp. 289–294)

**Finding the Main Idea** This reading strategy helps you organize and remember what you read. When you finish a selection, jot down the main idea and its supporting details.

1. **Read from the top of page 290 to the bottom of page 291. Which sentence below best expresses the main idea of the selection? Write an *M* next to your choice.**

   a. ___ Emperor Theodosius I divided the Roman Empire and gave half to each of his sons.

   b. ___ The Byzantine Empire was rich and powerful because it was a center of trade, religion, and education.

   c. ___ The Byzantine government set up schools and libraries, which led to a higher rate of literacy within the empire.

2. **Write one supporting detail for the main idea you chose in question 1.**

   _____

3. **Read from the top of page 292 to the bottom of 293. Which sentence below best expresses the main idea of the selection? Write an *M* next to your choice.**

   a. ___ The differences between the eastern and western branches of Christianity eventually led to a split.

   b. ___ The Holy Roman Emperor was the head of both church and state and thus held more power than the patriarch.

   c. ___ In 726, the Byzantine Emperor Leo III ordered that all religious icons be destroyed.

4. **Read the section "The Empire Under Attack" on page 294. Then fill in the chart below.**

| Main Idea | Supporting Details |
|---|---|
|  |  |

# Lesson 2 Summary
## The Byzantine Empire

*(Across the Centuries pp. 289–294)*

---

**Thinking Focus:** Compare the Eastern Orthodox Church and the Church of Rome.

## The Roman Empire in the East

Between 726 and 1095, Constantinople was the capital of the Byzantine or Eastern Roman Empire and a center of Christianity second only to Rome. The emperor's authority was believed to come from God.

A center of world trade, the government taxed everything that came into the empire. By 1000, one million people lived in Constantinople. Byzantine leaders had great respect for learning and the **classics**. The government set up schools and libraries and greatly increased the rate of **literacy**.

?  Why was the Byzantine Empire so powerful?

**classic**
(klăs'ĭk)
a work of art or literature from ancient Greece or Rome

**literacy**
(lĭt'ər-ə-sē)
the ability to read and write

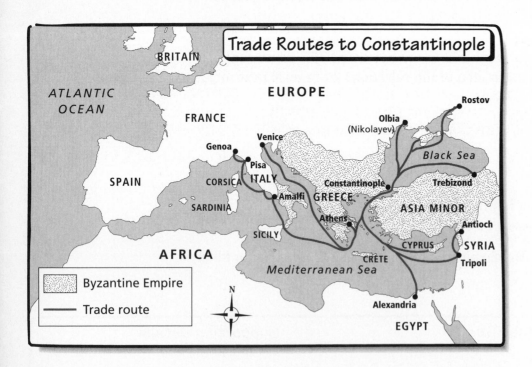

Trade Routes to Constantinople

- Byzantine Empire
- —— Trade route

*Summary continues on next page*

# The Eastern Church

The bishop who led the Byzantine church was called the **patriarch**. But the more powerful Byzantine emperor was head of both church and state. The churches in both the Eastern and Western empires were Christian. Yet their differences led to many disagreements, including a serious break over the use of **icons**. Then, in 800, the pope crowned the Franks' leader, Charlemagne, the first Holy Roman Emperor. This angered the Byzantines, who argued that only the Byzantine emperor should have power over them.

In 1054, the quarrel reached its height. The pope excommunicated the patriarch. In return, the patriarch excommunicated the pope. This led to a split, or **schism,** in the two churches. In the East was the Eastern Orthodox church. In the West was the Roman Catholic church.

**[?]** What factors led to the schism between the churches in the East and West?

**patriarch**
(pā′trē-ärk′)

in the Byzantine Empire, the bishop of Constantinople

**icon**
(ī′kŏn′)

picture or model of a sacred Christian person

**schism**
(sĭz′əm)

a split between two groups within a church

# The Empire Under Attack

The Byzantines kept a strong army because invaders kept taking over parts of the empire. In the 600s, Persians attacked from the east and south. In the 630s, Muslim Arabs attacked and captured the Empire's lands in Palestine and Syria. But throughout the 800s and 900s the Byzantines had peace. Then in 1071, the Seljuk Turks invaded and captured more and more land in present-day Turkey. By 1081 the Turks' capital was only 200 miles from Constantinople. In 1095, the Byzantine emperor was forced to ask an old enemy, the pope, for military help against the Turks.

**[?]** Why did the Byzantine Empire decline in power between the early 600s and late 700s?

CHAPTER 11

# Lesson 3 Preview
## The Crusades

(*Across the Centuries* pp. 295–302)

### Effects of the Crusades

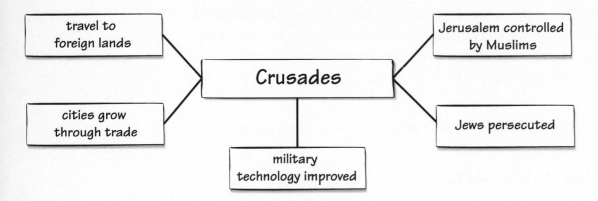

1. **Look at the graphic organizer above. Then read the following sentences and fill in the blanks.**

   a. What happened to Jerusalem in spite of the crusades?

   _____

   _____

   b. Name at least one positive thing that happened during the crusades.

   _____

   _____

2. **Look at the map on page 299 in your text. Which areas had been lost by the crusaders to the Muslims by 1187?**

   _____

   _____

   _____

   _____

   _____

CHAPTER 11

# Lesson 3 Reading Strategy
## The Crusades

*(Across the Centuries* pp. 295–302)

**Think About Words** This reading strategy helps you figure out the meaning of new words. When you come to an unfamiliar word, look for word parts you already know and use clues such as context and pictures.

1.  Read the section "The Christians' Motives" on pages 296–297. Then look back at the word *pilgrimage* on page 295. What part of the word *pilgrimage* is familiar?

    _____

2.  Look at the words around the word *pilgrimage*. What words give you context clues about what the word means?

    _____

    **What is a pilgrimage?**

    _____

3.  Read the section entitled "The Crusade of Kings" on page 300. Then fill in as much of the chart below as you can to help you figure out what the word means.

    **WORD:** Unstable

    Parts of the word I already know:
    _____

    Context clues from other words around it:
    _____

    Meaning:
    _____

    _____

# Lesson 3 Summary
## The Crusades

(*Across the Centuries* pp. 295–302)

**Thinking Focus:** What were the crusades, and why were they important?

## The Crusades Begin

The **crusades** were a series of eight wars that took place between 1096 and 1270. From the 900s, many European Christians had visited the Holy Land. They wanted to see the places where Jesus had lived. Around 1070, the region became unstable, and the pilgrim routes less safe. Some European leaders saw a chance to win the Holy Land. In 1095 the Pope called for a holy war against **infidels**, or non-Christians.

About 45,000 crusaders took part in the First Crusade. On their way they persecuted and killed any non-Christians they found. In 1097, the crusaders marched in and took over the capital of the Seljuk Turks. Then they moved east toward Jerusalem. The crusaders set up small states as they went. They ran these states like feudal kingdoms. In 1099, the crusaders reached Jerusalem. They defeated the Muslims and set up Jerusalem as the capital of a crusader state. For a time, the Holy Land was in Christian control.

**?** Why did the Christians want to capture Jerusalem?

**crusade**
(krōō-sād′)

a military movement by European Christians to win the Holy Land from the Muslims

**infidel**
(ĭn′fĭ-del)

a nonbeliever in Christianity

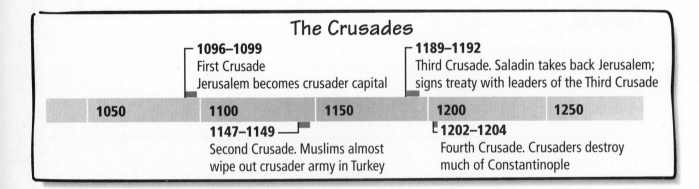

### The Crusades

**1096–1099**
First Crusade
Jerusalem becomes crusader capital

**1189–1192**
Third Crusade. Saladin takes back Jerusalem; signs treaty with leaders of the Third Crusade

| 1050 | 1100 | 1150 | 1200 | 1250 |

**1147–1149**
Second Crusade. Muslims almost wipe out crusader army in Turkey

**1202–1204**
Fourth Crusade. Crusaders destroy much of Constantinople

*Summary continues on next page*

Reading Support Resources

# Muslims Regain the Holy Land

In the 1140s the Muslims began to take back control of the Holy Land. Muslim forces nearly wiped out the second crusader army in Turkey, and went on to recapture more crusader land. In the late 1100s, Muslim leader Saladin led the Muslim forces against the crusaders at Tiberias. His army defeated the crusaders. Saladin then took back Jerusalem.

The Third Crusade was called by Germany, England, and France. In 1192, Saladin signed a treaty with the crusader army. This treaty allowed Christian pilgrims to visit the Holy Land and Muslims to control the region. A Fourth Crusade began in 1198. This time the crusaders approached by sea instead of by land. On their way, they tried to put a new Byzantine emperor in office. When the people of Constantinople rebelled, the crusaders destroyed much of the city.

? Were the crusades successful? Explain.

# The Crusades Affect the West

In many ways, the crusades were a failure for the Christians. They were a disaster for Jews, who suffered from persecution. But the crusades caused some positive changes in western Europe:

- **Trade** grew because of the crusaders' need for goods and services. And the crusades also gave western Europe more trade contacts in the Mediterranean world.

- **War technology** transferred from East to West. The crusaders had seen new ways of fighting in the Middle East.

- **Interest increased in music and poetry.** Arabic love poetry and music affected European crusaders.

- **Missionary activity.** The church came to see exploration as a way of spreading Christianity.

- **Feudalism grew weaker.** As thousands of feudal lords were killed, Europe's national governments grew stronger.

- **Opening up the world.** Contact with other cultures made people more willing to try new things.

? How did the crusades benefit western Europe?

# Chapter Overview
## The Renaissance

**Fill in the blanks below with information from the chapter.**

## Renaissance in Europe

### The End of the Middle Ages

**Military advances:** guns, gunpowder, harquebuses

**Valued goods:** _____

### Rebirth in Italy

**Great artists:** _____

**Humanist beliefs:** Individualism, Classicism, public service

### Renaissance Society

**Leading Renaissance City:** _____

**Guilds:** Blacksmiths, carpenters, tanners, butchers

### The Renaissance Moves North

**How ideas spread:** trade and travel, printing press

**Renaissance Achievements:** _____

**CHAPTER 12**

# Lesson 1 Preview

## Europe at the End of the Middle Ages

(*Across the Centuries* pp. 310–315)

### Europe at the End of the Middle Ages

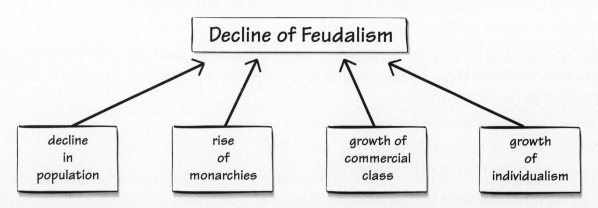

1. Look at the graphic organizer above. Then read the following list of factors that led to the decline of feudalism. If the factor increased, write an arrow up. If the factor decreased, write an arrow down.

   ____ population

   ____ individualism

   ____ commercial class

   ____ monarchies

2. Look at the picture on page 313. Then name or describe three weapons common at the end of the Middle Ages.

   _____

   _____

   _____

CHAPTER 12

# Lesson 1 Reading Strategy
## Europe at the End of the Middle Ages

*(Across the Centuries* pp. 310–315)

**Self-Question** This reading strategy helps you stay focused on what you read. Ask yourself questions before you read a section. Then read it to see if you can find the answers to your questions.

1.  **Read the heading "Europe in Crisis" on page 311. Which question do you expect to have answered in the paragraphs that follow this heading? Circle the letter next to the best answer.**

    a.  How did the crisis affect people of different social classes?

    b.  What were some achievements during the later Middle Ages?

    c.  Did Asia suffer from crisis when Europe did?

    **Now read the section to see if the question you chose was answered. If it was, write the answer to the question.**

    _____

2.  **Look at the map on page 311. Then read the key and the caption. Which question asks about the regions shown there? Circle the letter next to the best answer.**

    a.  What areas were the first and last to be hit by the Great Plague?

    b.  Why was Europe hit by the Great Plague?

    c.  When and where did the Great Plague end?

3.  **Read the heading "Trade and Commerce" on page 314. Then read the questions on the following chart. Now read the section and fill in the answers to the questions as you find them.**

| Ask Yourself | Answers |
|---|---|
| Why did Italy prosper as a trade center? | |
| What goods did Italian traders buy and sell? | |
| How did international trade change the values of medieval society? | |

# Lesson 1 Summary
## Europe at the End of the Middle Ages

*(Across the Centuries pp. 310–315)*

**Thinking Focus:** How did the problems of the 14th century bring about changes in European society?

## Europe in Crisis

From around the year 1000 until 1315, the population of Europe more than doubled. It was hard for farmers to raise enough food for this large population. Food supplies ran short. Then disaster struck. Heavy rains from 1315 to 1319 caused food to rot in the fields. Thousands of people starved to death. Then, in 1347, a terrible **plague** moved from China across Asia and fell upon the people of Europe. People later called it the Black Death. It struck again in 1360 and 1374. By the late 1300s, one-fourth to one-third of the population had died.

After the plague, there were fewer workers. With fewer people to do the work, peasants began to demand better pay and lower rent. When landlords refused, some peasants rebelled. Other peasants moved to towns or villages so they could be free of the landlords. Some landlords passed laws to force peasants to work for their old wages. Many peasants joined together to burn the houses of the landlords. Medieval ways were crumbling.

**plague**
(plăg)

a disease that spreads and is usually deadly

**monarchy**
(mŏn´ər-kē)

a strong central government ruled by a king or queen

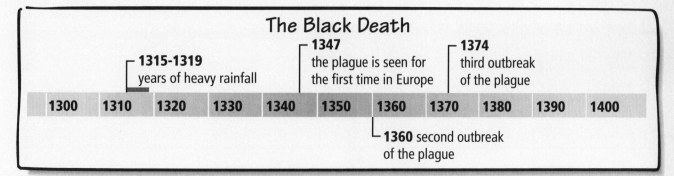

**The Black Death**

**1315-1319**
years of heavy rainfall

**1347**
the plague is seen for the first time in Europe

**1374**
third outbreak of the plague

| 1300 | 1310 | 1320 | 1330 | 1340 | 1350 | 1360 | 1370 | 1380 | 1390 | 1400 |

**1360** second outbreak of the plague

[?] How did the plague affect the society and economy of western Europe?

*Summary continues on next page*

# Rise of Central Governments

During the late Middle Ages, power was slowly slipping away from the nobles who owned feudal estates. Kings were starting to form **monarchies** with strong governments. As they gained power, kings and queens collected taxes, formed armies, and ruled the people.

In the 1300s and 1400s, many nobles fought wars against the kings. New weapons changed the way wars were fought. Armies used longbows, which could pierce through armor. Later, they used cannons and handguns. The longest war during the late Middle Ages was the Hundred Years' War between the French and the English. It began in 1337. The war raged on and off for 116 years, until finally the French won. At one point, when it seemed like the French were losing, Joan of Arc went to see Charles, the future French king. She was a peasant girl who convinced him that God had sent her to defeat the English. Joan of Arc won five battles against the English. After two years of fighting, she was captured. She was tried as a witch and **heretic** by the English and the Church. At age 19, she was burned at the stake.

[?] Why did the feudal system begin to crumble?

# Trade and Commerce

Trade and commerce grew in the late Middle Ages. Italian towns like Florence and Milan became wealthy from the new intercontinental trade with Asia, Africa, and the rest of Europe. These towns traded cotton, silk, wool, wine, fur, feathers, jewels, ivory, metals, and spices.

Some of the richest Italian merchants were bankers and moneylenders. They lent money to kings and popes. More importantly, they worked for themselves. Their freedom and success changed the values of the medieval world. **Individualism** became a popular value. People wanted to be free to set and pursue their own goals.

[?] How did medieval values change as trade and commerce grew?

**heretic**
(hĕr´ĭ-tĭk)

a person who speaks opinions that disagree with the beliefs of the Roman Catholic Church

**individualism**
(ĭn´də-vĭj´oo-ə-lĭz´əm)

personal independence; the idea that every person should be free to set his or her own goals

CHAPTER 12

# Lesson 2 Preview
## The Italian Renaissance

*(Across the Centuries pp. 316–323)*

## Causes and Effects of the Italian Renaissance

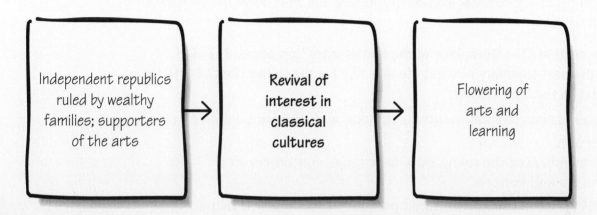

Independent republics ruled by wealthy families; supporters of the arts → Revival of interest in classical cultures → Flowering of arts and learning

1. **Look at the graphic organizer above. Then read the following descriptions. Identify each description as a cause, effect, or cause and effect of the Renaissance.**

   ____ Independent republics ruled by wealthy families; supporters of the arts

   ____ Flowering of arts and learning

   ____ Revival of interest in classical cultures

2. **Look at the photographs in this lesson. Then complete this phrase: The Renaissance was a time of**

   _____

   _____

   _____

   _____

   _____

   _____

   _____

CHAPTER 12

# Lesson 2 Reading Strategy
## The Italian Renaissance

(*Across the Centuries* pp. 316–323)

**Summarize** This reading strategy helps you remember key points about what you have read. When you get to a good break in your reading, stop and write down the main ideas of what you have read.

1. Read the section "The Birthplace of the Renaissance" on pages 317–318. What is the best summary of what life was like for the ruling class? Circle the letter next to the best answer.

   **a.** The ruling class lived in luxurious palaces, with servants, scholars, and artists.

   **b.** Some members of the ruling class were kings, but others were merchants and bankers.

   **c.** Members of the ruling class hired mercenaries to fight for them.

2. Read the section "The Renaissance and Life" on pages 318–319. What is the best summary of humanist values? Circle the letter next to the best answer.

   **a.** Humanists believed the classical arts included literature and philosophy.

   **b.** Humanists believed humans could improve themselves by studying classics.

   **c.** Humanists believed in human goodness, public service, and a well-rounded education.

3. Read the section "The Flowering of Arts and Learning" on pages 319–323. Summarize why Leonardo da Vinci was the ideal Renaissance man.

   _____

   _____

4. Read the section "Wealth and the Renaissance." Then use the space below to summarize the information contained in the section.

   _____

   _____

   _____

   _____

   _____

   _____

# Lesson 2 Summary
## The Italian Renaissance

*(Across the Centuries pp. 316–323)*

**Thinking Focus:** In what ways did viewpoints about human beings change during the Renaissance?

## The Birthplace of the Renaissance

The **Renaissance** began in northern Italy. In the late Middle Ages, Italy was made of about 250 city-states. Some of these city-states were **republics** ruled by rich aristocrats and merchant families. The Medici family was one of the richest and most powerful. Families like the Medicis used their money to beautify their cities. They had their own courts which included the best artists and scholars.

Rulers of different city-states competed for land and power. They hired **mercenaries** to fight their battles. Politics were cruel, too. Political adviser Niccolò Machiavelli told his prince to ignore questions of good and evil. He argued that rulers should do whatever is necessary to improve their states.

**?** Why did the Renaissance begin in Northern Italy?

## The Renaissance and Life

People in the city-states wanted to understand the arts. They studied Greek and Roman classics, or humanities. Their studies became known as **humanism**. Medieval Christians saw themselves as sinners. Humanists did not see people as sinful. They thought people had dignity and worth. They were more interested in life on Earth than heaven or hell. Humanists focused on three classical ideas. They believed in the individual worth of people. They also had a strong commitment to public service. They supported public buildings and funding the arts. And they encouraged people to develop their own skills and talents and have interests in many different subjects.

**?** What were the basic beliefs held by Renaissance humanists?

---

**Renaissance**
(rĕn´ĭ-säns´)
a revival of interest in ideas from ancient Greek and Roman art, literature, and learning

**republic**
(rĭ-pŭb´lĭk)
a political order in which elected citizens are rulers

**mercenary**
(mûr´sə-nĕrē)
a professional soldier hired by a foreign country

**humanism**
(hyoo´mə-nĭz´əm)
a set of attitudes or beliefs that center on human beings and their values, abilities, and achievements

---

*Summary continues on next page*

# The Flowering of Arts and Learning

The Renaissance was a time of art and learning. The Italian artist Leonardo da Vinci painted the *Mona Lisa* and other great paintings. He also was one of the greatest scientific thinkers of his day. Italian writers Francesco Petrarch and Giovanni Boccaccio discovered ancient Greek and Roman writings. They borrowed the graceful style of the classical writers.

New ideas and technology spread throughout Europe. This shaped the ideas of other Renaissance men. Florence architect Filippo Brunelleschi used a new technique in art. He used a linear perspective in his work to make a flat, painted surface look 3-D. He also studied ancient building styles. He designed and built the Florence cathedral with a Roman-style dome. Many Renaissance artists combined the old and new. They developed a better way to blend paints by using oil. They also adopted the **realism** of ancient Greece and Rome. They made their paintings and sculptures look lifelike. Some of these paintings had religious subjects. Others were portraits, country scenes, and battles.

**[?]** How did Renaissance humanism lead to achievements in the arts and sciences?

**realism**
(rē′ə-lĭz′əm)

an artistic style that aims to show people as they really are

# Wealth and the Renaissance

The Renaissance was started by upper-class Italians. They could read and write and had free time. They spent their time studying the ideas of ancient Greeks and Romans. In addition, wealthy Italians were involved in trade. In this way, they learned about other peoples and ideas. They also had enough money to spend on art.

For scholars, painters, and art lovers, the Renaissance was a very exciting time. For most people, however, life went on as usual. They could not read or afford to buy art. They spent most of their time simply earning a living.

**[?]** How important was wealth in fostering the Renaissance?

**CHAPTER 12**

# Lesson 3 Preview
## Renaissance Life

*(Across the Centuries pp. 325–328)*

### City-states in the Renaissance

|  | Employment | % of Population |
|---|---|---|
| **Upper Class** | merchants, bankers | 2 |
| **Commercial Class** | shopkeepers, artisans | 23 |
| **Lower Class** | laborers, farmers, and unemployed | 75 |

1. **Look at the graphic organizer above. Use the following words to fill in the blanks below.**

   | farmers | bankers | shopkeepers | artisans |

   a. During the Renaissance, most people worked as laborers and

   _____.

   b. Almost one-quarter of the population were _____ and

   _____.

2. **Look at the picture at the bottom of page 326 in your text. Complete the sentence by naming the correct city.**

   The city of _____ featured paved streets, beautiful public buildings, and a domed cathedral.

CHAPTER 12

# Lesson 3 Reading Strategy
## Renaissance Life

(*Across the Centuries* pp. 325–328)

**Compare and Contrast** This reading strategy helps you understand how events are similar and different. As you read about historical events, think about how they compare and contrast with events you already know.

1. Read from the top of page 325 to the heading "The Renaissance City." Which of the following pairs best show the contrast between winning and losing the *palio* at Florence? Circle the letter next to the best answer.

   a. street procession/race
   b. riders risk their lives/riders gallop bareback
   c. glory and applause/broken spirits and broken bones

2. Read the section "From Peasant to Patrician" on pages 326–327. Then fill in the chart below with information describing peasants and patricians.

| Peasants | Patricians |
|---|---|
|  |  |
|  |  |
|  |  |
|  |  |

3. Read the section "The Importance of Family" on pages 327–328. Write a sentence comparing the education of upper-class men and women.

   _____

4. Name one way in which the lives of upper-class women and middle-class women were different.

   _____

# Lesson 3 Summary
## Renaissance Life

*(Across the Centuries* pp. 325–328)

Summary also on Audiotape

**Thinking Focus:** How did each of the social classes contribute to the Renaissance in Italy?

## The Renaissance City

The cities of Renaissance Italy were lively and colorful. Florence was one of the largest cities in Europe. More than 38,000 people lived there. Another 200,000 people lived in the nearby countryside. Florence and other cities built broad, paved streets and tall, narrow buildings. Many cities had plazas, cathedrals, and public buildings. The wealthy often lived right next door to the very poor.

The cities were very crowded. Violent quarrels were common. At night, the gates of the walled city were closed. Only those with special passes were allowed on the streets after dark.

What were some of the advantages and disadvantages of living in a Renaissance city?

## From Peasant to Patrician

People in the city-states belonged to many different social classes:

- The lower classes made up most of Florence's population. They included peasants, laborers, porters, and peddlers.

- The commercial or middle class was made up of shopkeepers. Artisans, like blacksmiths and carpenters, were also part of this class. They belonged to minor guilds.

- The upper class were **patricians**. Most were merchants and businesspeople. Bankers, lawyers, and doctors also formed guilds. Patricians and their families governed the cities. Many also were **patrons** of the arts.

**patrician**
(pə-trish′ən)

a member of the upper class in a Renaissance city-state; an aristocrat

**patron**
(pā′trən)

a person who gives financial support to scholars or artists

*Summary continues on next page*

Jews in Renaissance times were barred from most occupations. In the 1500s, governments began ordering Jews to live in separate neighborhoods, or ghettos. There they carried on their own community life.

**[?]** Describe the people who made up the lower, middle, and upper classes in Renaissance Italy.

### Social Classes in Renaissance Italy

| Class | Employment | Guild |
|---|---|---|
| Lower | porters, boatmen, peddlers, unemployed | no guilds |
| Commercial | shopkeepers, blacksmiths, tanners, carpenters, butchers | minor guilds |
| Patrician | rich merchants, bankers, doctors, lawyers | major guild association |

## The Importance of Family

The family was the center of patrician life. Family members were loyal to each other. Grandparents, aunts, uncles, cousins, parents, and children lived together in high-walled palaces. Upper-class men went to school, then traveled to learn the family business. Their parents arranged their marriages. Members of the bride's family had to provide a **dowry**. Women who could not afford a dowry often could not marry. Some joined convents.

Upper-class women were often forced to stay at home. Like Greek and Roman women, they had to care for their homes and children. Many learned to read, like Cassandra Fedele, who became a public speaker. Middle- and lower-class women continued to work in the trades. They prospered with the growth in the economy.

**[?]** Why was the family so important in Renaissance life?

**dowry**
(dou′rē)

money, land, servants or other valuable property a bride's family gives her husband at marriage.

CHAPTER 12

# Lesson 4 Preview
## Renaissance in Northern Europe

(*Across the Centuries* pp. 329–333)

### The Renaissance Spreads

|  | Beginning | Primary Supporters | Character |
|---|---|---|---|
| **Italian Renaissance** | 1300s | patrician families | secular |
| **Northern Renaissance** | late 1400s | royal courts | religious |

1. **Look at the graphic organizer above. Then read the following sentences. Write an *I* next to a sentence that describes the Italian Renaissance. Write an *N* next to a sentence that describes the Northern Renaissance.**

   ___ a. It was supported by patrician families.

   ___ b. It took place mostly at court.

   ___ c. It began in the 1300s and caused the Renaissance to spread throughout Europe.

   ___ d. It was mostly secular in character.

2. **Look at the map on page 330 in your text. Then describe the extent of the Medici family's trade route. Name the European cities in which the Medicis traded.**

   _____

   _____

   _____

   _____

   _____

   _____

CHAPTER 12

# Lesson 4 Reading Strategy
## Renaissance in Northern Europe

(*Across the Centuries* pp. 329–333)

**Cause and Effect** This reading strategy help you understand events and why they occur. As you read, think about the factors that caused an event. Then think about what the effects of that event might be.

1. Read the section "The Spread of Ideas" on pages 330–331. Which of the following was <u>not</u> a cause of the spread of the Renaissance? Circle the letter next to the best answer.

   a. the courts and the church

   b. artists and scholars

   c. traders, travelers, and books

2. What was the effect of movable type?

   _____

3. Read the section "Ideas and Ideals" on pages 331–332. What was the effect of church support during the northern Renaissance?

   _____

4. Read the section "Achievements" on pages 332–333. Then fill in the chart below.

| Cause | Effect |
|---|---|
| Sir Thomas More adopts the concept of individual worth | |
| | His characters are full of life, wit, and passion. |
| New firearms cause new kinds of injuries | |

# Lesson 4 Summary
## Renaissance in Northern Europe

(*Across the Centuries* pp. 329–333)

**Thinking Focus:** How was the northern European Renaissance different from the Italian Renaissance?

## The Spread of Ideas

Renaissance ideas began to spread to northern Europe in the late 1400s. Europeans admired the Italian focus on wealth, beauty, and achievement.

Between 1438 and 1454, Johannes Gutenberg, a German, invented a printing press with movable type. By 1500, printers had made between 9 and 12 million books. People learned to read the Bible and Roman and Greek classics. They also read works by humanist writers of the time. Kings and queens adopted humanist values. They began supporting scholars and artists. By the mid-1500s, Renaissance ideals were a part of northern European culture.

? How did the ideas of the Italian Renaissance spread to northern Europe?

European Trade Routes

*Summary continues on next page*

# Ideas and Ideals

Northern humanism was different from Italian humanism. In northern Europe, nobles and royalty had most of the wealth and power. These people studied the arts. In northern Europe, most Renaissance learning happened at court. The court became the center of culture.

Northern Europe also had fewer towns. Like the Italians, the northern Europeans valued **secular** ideas. But they also focused on religious life. They studied Greek and Hebrew in order to read the Bible in the original languages. Some northern Europeans began to question church customs. A Dutch priest named Desiderius Erasmus believed church teaching should be easy. He also thought everyone should be able to read the Bible. Erasmus wrote many books, and traveled around Europe, to spread his ideas.

> **secular**
> (sĕk′yə-lər)
> worldly, rather than religious

**[?]** Did northern humanism stress the spiritual or the secular? Explain.

# Achievements

Artists like Jan Van Eyck painted both people and nature more realistically. Writers talked about religion, politics, and human behavior. Scientists made important discoveries.

Thomas More was an important English artist and thinker. In his book, *Utopia,* More said that all men should be treated equally. William Shakespeare, the English playwright, created characters who had the life, wit, and passions of real people.

Paracelsus was a Swiss doctor and chemist. He found a new way to treat patients. He gave them tiny doses of poison to help destroy diseases. Ambroise Paré was a French doctor and surgeon. He created bandages. Now doctors did not have to burn wounds to seal them. Paré also was the first to use thread to close a wound.

**[?]** Describe some of the achievements of the northern Renaissance.

# Chapter Overview
## Reformation and the Scientific Revolution

**Fill in the blanks with information from the chapter.**

**When:**
1302–1687

**Where:**
Western Europe

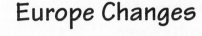

Europe Changes

Wycliffe translates Bible — **Late 1300s**

**1520** — Pope Leo X excommunicates Martin Luther

_____ **1540s**

**1543** Copernicus publishes life's work

Calvin dies ——————

**1616** Church condemns Galileo

Bacon publishes Novum Organum — **1620**

**1687** _____

_____

CHAPTER 13
# Lesson 1 Preview
## The Decline of Church Authority

*(Across the Centuries pp. 338–341)*

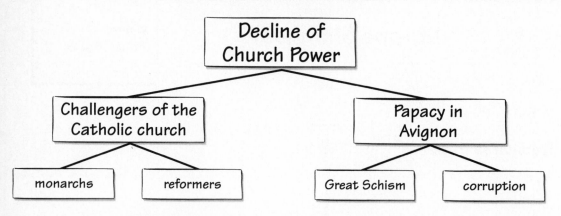

### The Church Loses Power

```
              Decline of
            Church Power

   Challengers of the        Papacy in
   Catholic church            Avignon

  monarchs   reformers    Great Schism   corruption
```

1. **Look at the graphic organizer above. Read the following sentences and fill in the blanks.**

   During the 1500s, the Catholic church declined in _____. Both

   monarchs and _____ challenged the church. The pope moved

   his residence (the papacy) to Avignon, France. This led to corruption and

   the Great _____ in the church.

2. **Look at the picture of the gold cross covered in jewels on page 338 in your text. What does this item tell you about the church in the 1500s?**

   _____

   _____

   _____

CHAPTER 13

# Lesson 1 Reading Strategy
## The Decline of Church Authority

(*Across the Centuries* pp. 338–341)

**Evaluate** This reading strategy helps you recognize the difference between facts and opinions. A fact is something that can be proven to be true. An opinion is a belief based on what a person thinks or feels.

1. **Read the introductory material on page 338 above the heading "Conflicts over Power." Which statement below is a fact? Circle the letter next to the best answer.**

    a. Everyone thought the church was too powerful.

    b. King Philip IV damaged the authority of the church.

    c. The pope wanted to crush the king's power.

2. **Read the section "Conflicts over Power" on pages 338–340. Which statement below is an opinion? Circle the letter next to the best answer.**

    a. The Italian city-states thought that the popes were controlled by France.

    b. The Great Schism weakened the church's authority.

    c. Pope Clement V was too cautious.

3. **Read the section "The Call for Church Reform" on pages 340–341. Then read the statements in the chart below and decide whether each is a fact or an opinion. Write *fact* or *opinion* next to each statement.**

| | |
|---|---|
| The church punished heretics. | |
| People depended on the clergy to interpret the Latin Bible | |

4. **As you read the lesson, evaluate the church's authority. Then write your own opinion of the church's authority.**

    _____

    _____

# Lesson 1 Summary
## The Decline of Church Authority

(*Across the Centuries* pp. 338–341)

**Thinking Focus:** What challenges did the Catholic church face between 1300 and 1500? Why?

## Conflicts over Power

The kings and popes of Europe struggled with each other for power during the 1300s. Millions of Europeans were Christians and followed the leadership of the pope. However, the French king Philip IV did not want the pope to be so powerful.

In 1305, the church tried to make peace with the French king by choosing a French pope, Clement V. Clement decided to live in France instead of Italy. This upset other European rulers.

After 70 years, Pope Gregory XI moved the pope's residence back to Rome, Italy. The next pope was Italian. The French were not happy with this pope. They elected their own pope who lived in France. At that point, Europe had two popes. This division became known as the Great Schism.

The Great Schism weakened the church's power. Many of the church leaders wanted to find a way to make the church strong again. During the 1400s, these church leaders met together in **councils.** The purpose of these councils was to decide on religious laws and matters of faith. One council, the Council of Constance, united the church under one pope again.

The reunited church was not as strong as it used to be for many reasons. One reason was that the European kings had power over the councils. Another reason was that some church leaders were not honest. They sold **indulgences** to people who thought they had sinned. Jobs were also sold by the church. A person with money could buy a job in the church.

**?** How did the conflict between kings and popes lead to the Great Schism?

**council**
(koun´səl)

a series of meetings of Roman Catholic church leaders in the 1400s dealing with issues of church law and faith

**indulgence**
(ĭn-dŭl´jəns)

a paper from the pope that was said to reduce or cancel punishment for a person's sins

*Summary continues on next page*

## Church Problems and Reforms

| Church Problems | Demands of Reformers |
|---|---|
| • sale of indulgences | • called for monarchs to rule over church |
| • collection of taxes and other fines | • translated Bible from Latin to local languages |
| • sale of jobs in the church | • demanded an end to sale of indulgences |
| • some corrupt clergy | • challenged church's authority |
| • punishment of heretics | |

# The Call for Church Reform

By the 1300s, many people felt that the church leaders were not following the ideals set forth in the Bible. People began to call for reforms, or changes, in the church. One of these reformers was John Wycliffe of England. He said that kings should rule over the church in their own kingdoms. He also translated the Bible from Latin into English. With the English version of the Bible, people in England could read the Bible themselves without the help of the clergy.

However, it could be dangerous to challenge the church. Another reformer, the priest John Hus of eastern Europe, spoke out against the selling of indulgences. The church called him a heretic. This meant his views were not accepted by the church. As punishment, he was burned at the stake. His death kept many people from disagreeing with the church in public.

Other groups such as the mystics wanted to express religious feelings in their own way. The mystics felt that people could experience God directly in their hearts. They also believed that both men and women could experience God.

**?** What church doctrine did the early reformers oppose?

# CHAPTER 13

# Lesson 2 Preview

## Martin Luther and the Reformation

*(Across the Centuries pp. 342–347)*

### Changes in the Christian Church

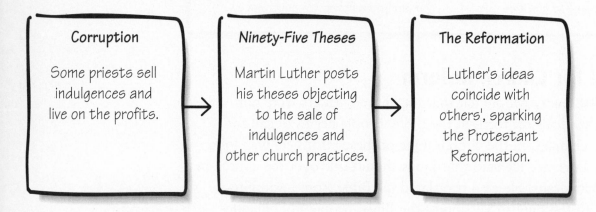

| Corruption | | Ninety-Five Theses | | The Reformation |
|---|---|---|---|---|
| Some priests sell indulgences and live on the profits. | → | Martin Luther posts his theses objecting to the sale of indulgences and other church practices. | → | Luther's ideas coincide with others', sparking the Protestant Reformation. |

1. **Look at the graphic organizer above. Then read the following sentences. Write *T* next to a sentence that is true. Write *F* next to a sentence that is false.**

   _____ **a.** Some priests were making a living by selling indulgences.

   _____ **b.** Luther's ideas led to the Great Schism.

   _____ **c.** Martin Luther was the only person to object to priests selling indulgences.

   _____ **d.** Many other people must have agreed with Martin Luther.

2. **Look at the photographs and illustrations in this lesson as well as the red titles. Why do you think pages 345 and 346 show a printing press and a printer?**

   _____

   _____

   _____

   _____

   _____

   _____

   _____

CHAPTER 13

# Lesson 2 Reading Strategy
## Martin Luther and the Reformation

(*Across the Centuries* pp. 342–347)

**Summarize** This reading strategy helps you remember key points about what you have read. When you get to a good break in your reading, stop and write down the main ideas of what you have read.

1. **Read the first three paragraphs of the section "Luther Questions the Church" on page 343. What is the best summary of what life was like for Martin Luther? Circle the letter next to the best answer.**

   a. Luther was studying to become a lawyer.

   b. Luther's father wanted him to become a lawyer.

   c. Luther believed that God helped him so he should become a monk.

2. **Read the section "A New Religion" on pages 343–344. Which of the following is the best summary of Luther's beliefs? Circle the letter next to the best answer.**

   a. Luther believed that only God, not the church, could grant forgiveness.

   b. Luther believed that priests could sell indulgences only if they had the pope's approval.

   c. Luther believed that individuals could receive forgiveness by performing religious rituals and doing good deeds.

3. **Read the section "The Reformation Begins" on pages 344–345. Fill in the rest of the chart that summarizes the information contained in the section.**

| Luther's Actions | Efforts to Stop Luther |
|---|---|
| a. Luther writes hundreds of essays. | |
| b. Luther publicly burns Pope Leo's bull. | |
| c. _____ | The emperor declares Luther an outlaw. |

# Lesson 2 Summary

## Martin Luther and the Reformation

(*Across the Centuries* pp. 342–347)

Summary also on Audiotape

---

**Thinking Focus:** What was Luther's role in the Reformation?

## Luther Questions the Church

Martin Luther was born in Germany in 1483. He trained to become a lawyer, but gave that up in order to become a monk. By 1507, he was a priest.

But Luther struggled with some of the church's practices and teachings. The church taught that a person could save his soul by following religious practices and by doing good deeds. Luther questioned whether these things were enough to please God.

Luther found the answers to his questions in a letter written by St. Paul. St. Paul wrote that faith in God was the only way a person could save his soul. This belief, known as justification by faith, meant that the church did not have the right to pardon, or excuse, people for their sins; only God did.

Luther believed that the church's practice of selling indulgences was wrong. He wrote his *Ninety-Five Theses* to protest the dishonesty of some of the clergy. He invited scholars to debate these ideas. But his invitation had a much bigger effect. It sparked a movement to reform the Catholic church. People who joined this protest against the church became known as **Protestants**. The movement was called the **Reformation**.

? How did Martin Luther's beliefs conflict with church doctrine and practices?

**Protestant**
(prŏt′ĭ-stənt)

a reformer who protested against the abuses of the Catholic church in the 1500s; a member of a church that separated from the Catholic church during the 1500s

**Reformation**
(rĕf′ər-mā′shən)

the reform movement of the 1500s that resulted in the separation of the Protestant churches from the Roman Catholic church

*Summary continues on next page*

# The Reformation Begins

Luther's *Ninety-Five Theses* were translated from Latin into German so that everyone could understand them. Luther continued to attack the church in hundreds of essays. He also wrote about justification by faith. In 1520, the pope issued a statement against Luther and banned his teachings. Luther burned the statement. The pope excommunicated Luther. This means the pope cut off Luther from the church. The Holy Roman Emperor tried to give Luther another chance. He asked Luther to take back his teachings. When Luther refused, the emperor declared that Luther was an outlaw.

For one year, Luther hid in a castle. He used this time to translate the Bible from Greek into German. He also wrote more essays against the Catholic church. His teachings soon led to the creation of a separate Lutheran church.

[?] How effective were the church's responses to Luther's teachings?

# Protestantism Spreads

Many people accepted Protestantism. They wanted to reform the church and stop corruption. It was also a time of change. New ideas that came with increased trade showed people that change was possible. Also, in the mid-1400s, the printing press was developed. This allowed Luther's work to be spread quickly in **pamphlets**.

Luther believed in strong rulers and a weaker church. Some German princes liked Luther's ideas. They wanted to be free of the church's power. Other German princes remained Catholics. Fighting erupted between the Protestant and Catholic German princes. In 1555, the princes agreed to work together and end the fighting. This was called the Peace of Augsburg. This allowed each prince to choose the religion for his state and his people. Most states in northern Germany became Protestant. The southern states chose to remain Catholic.

[?] Why did Protestantism spread throughout Germany between 1517 and 1560?

**pamphlet**
(păm′flĭt)

an unbound published work, such as an essay, usually on a current topic

CHAPTER 13
# Lesson 3 Preview
## Era of Reformation
*(Across the Centuries pp. 349–352)*

### The Reformation

Protestant Movements
- Lutheranism
- Calvinism
- Anabaptist movement
- Church of England

Many people leave the Catholic church to join Protestant movements.

Counter Reformation
- Council of Trent
- Founding of new orders
- The Inquisition

1. **Look at the graphic organizer above. Then read the following sentences. Write *T* next to a sentence that is true. Write *F* next to a sentence that is false.**

   ____ **a.** Many Protestants returned to the Catholic church.

   ____ **b.** There were many different Protestant groups.

   ____ **c.** The Catholic church responded to the Protestant movements by starting the Counter Reformation.

   ____ **d.** The Council of Trent was just one of the many Protestant movements.

2. **Look at the chart on page 350 in your text. Then read the following sentences and fill in the blanks.**

   Popes were the founders of the _____ church. Other churches

   founded during the Reformation were the _____ church in

   1529 and the _____ in 1534. In _____, John

   Calvin founded the Calvinist church.

CHAPTER 13

# Lesson 3 Reading Strategy
## Era of Reformation

(*Across the Centuries* pp. 349–352)

**Sequence** This reading strategy helps you follow the order of events. As you read, pay attention to dates and times, as well as to words such as *before, finally, after,* and *then.*

1. Read the section "Calvin and the Reformation" on pages 349–350. Find at least two words or phrases that help you understand the sequence of events.

   _____

   _____

2. Read the section "Other Protestant Movements" on pages 350–351. Place the following events in order by writing 1, 2, and 3 in the blanks.

   ____ Edward VI becomes king.

   ____ Anabaptist movement begins in Zurich.

   ____ Henry VIII argues with the pope about Henry's wish for a divorce.

3. Read the section "The Church's Response" on pages 351–352. Place the folllowing events in order by writing 1, 2, and 3 in the blanks.

   ____ Ignatius Loyola founds the Society of Jesus.

   ____ The Council of Trent is held.

   ____ Catholic priests begin to recognize that reforms are needed in the church.

4. As you read the lesson, fill in the timeline below.

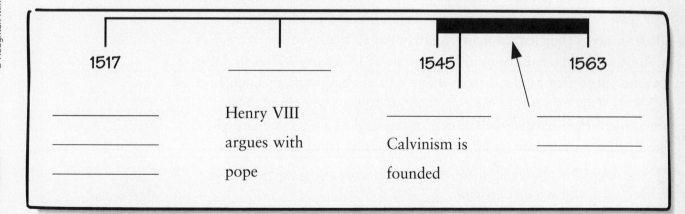

# Lesson 3 Summary
## Era of Reformation

(*Across the Centuries* pp. 349–352)

Summary also on Audiotape

**Thinking Focus:** What effect did the Reformation have on religion in Europe?

## Calvin and the Reformation

In the early 1500s, the Reformation spread throughout Europe. John Calvin was a Frenchman living in Geneva, Switzerland. He taught the people of this city to read and study the Bible on their own. Soon, Geneva became the center of a new Protestant movement called Calvinism.

One idea that Calvin taught was that God had chosen a special group of people for salvation. Luther also believed in this theory, known as **predestination**. But Luther believed that people could never know whom God had chosen.

The Calvinists lived a strict moral life. To them, this meant that they must not gamble, go to fortune tellers, or dance at social events. Their churches did not have statues or paintings. Their services were held quietly without organ music. They could not do anything that got in the way of their relationship to God.

> **predestination**
> (prē-dĕs′tə-nā′shən)
> the belief that God has determined all things in advance, including the salvation of souls

**?** What religious ideas and practices were important to Calvinists?

## Other Protestant Movements

There were many other Protestant groups. One group, the Anabaptists, believed that most people were sinners, and the state was made up of sinners. They wanted to withdraw from the state and form their own community. Catholics and Protestants did not like being called sinners. They forced many Anabaptists to flee.

Another movement began in England in 1533. Henry VIII asked his government to free England from the rule of anybody but an English authority. This meant that the pope had no power in England. The government then created the Church of England as a separate church. The English monarch was named the head of this church.

**?** Find evidence to support this statement: Some Protestant groups wanted to make political as well as religious reforms.

*Summary continues on next page*

## Major Churches During the Reformation

| Church | Time Founded | Founders | Administrators |
|---|---|---|---|
| Roman Catholic | 500s | Popes | Pope, Bishops, Councils |
| Lutheran | 1529 | Martin Luther | Congregation, Local Rulers |
| Church of England | 1534 | Henry VIII | King of England |
| Calvinist | 1546 | John Calvin | Presbytery (Council of Elders) |

# The Catholic Church's Response

Many Catholics knew that the church needed to be reformed. The church leaders begged the pope to do something. In the years 1545 to 1563, the church officials met in a series of meetings known as the Council of Trent. They wanted to stop corruption within the church and return to traditional Catholic beliefs. This movement within the church became known as the **Counter Reformation**.

The Counter Reformation worked to spread Catholic beliefs. New religious groups were formed, such as the Jesuits. The Catholics also formed the **Inquisition**. This was a church court that judged and punished people who went against the Catholics. Even non-Christians, such as Jews and Muslims, were persecuted. If these people would not become Catholics, they were tortured, killed, or sent out of the country. The church also made a list of books that people were not allowed to read.

[?] In what ways did the Catholic church try to reform from within?

**Counter Reformation**
(koun´tər ref´ər-mā´shən)

the reform movement within the Roman Catholic church whose goals were to get rid of abuses and return to traditional beliefs

**Inquisition**
(ĭn´kwĭ-zish´ən)

a Roman Catholic church court that was created to try and convict heretics, people who were against the Catholic church

# Lesson 4 Preview
## Scientific Revolution
(*Across the Centuries* pp. 353–356)

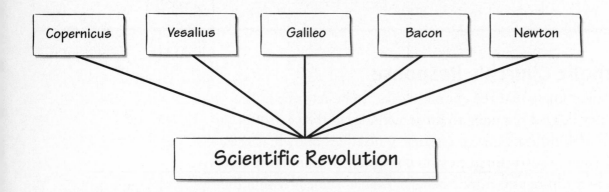

## Leaders of the Scientific Revolution

1. **Look at the graphic organizer above. Then read the following sentences and fill in the blanks.**

   Copernicus, _____, _____, Bacon, and

   _____ were all contributors to the _____
   Revolution.

2. **Look at the picture and read the caption on page 353 in your text. Then answer the following questions:**

   Whose system is shown in the picture, and what is shown at the center of the universe?

   _____

   _____

   In Ptolemy's system, what is at the center of the universe?

   _____

   _____

   Looking at the rest of the pictures in the lesson, what other advances do you think were made during the Scientific Revolution?

   _____

   _____

CHAPTER 13

# Lesson 4 Reading Strategy
## Scientific Revolution

(*Across the Centuries* pp. 353–356)

**Compare and Contrast** This reading strategy helps you understand how events are similar and different. As you read about historical events, think about how they compare and contrast with events you already know.

1. Read the first three paragraphs of the section "New Visions of the Natural World" on page 354. Compare Copernicus's theory of the universe with that of the Catholic church.

| a. Copernicus's claim | |
|---|---|
| b. Catholic church's claim | |

2. Read the rest of the section "New Visions of the Natural World" on page 354. Which sentence below is the best comparison of the work of Vesalius and Copernicus? Circle the letter next to the best answer.

   a. Copernicus and Vesalius explored the human body in similar ways.

   b. Copernicus and Vesalius both dared to question and reevaluate accepted theories.

   c. Copernicus and Vesalius explored planetary motion.

3. Read the first paragraph of the section "Galileo and the Church" on page 354. Write a sentence explaining one way that the work of Galileo was similar to that of Copernicus and Vesalius.

   _____

4. Read the section "The Scientific Method" on pages 355–356. Write two sentences comparing and contrasting the theories and beliefs about the physical world.

   _____

   _____

# Lesson 4 Summary
## Scientific Revolution

(*Across the Centuries* pp. 353–356)

---

**Thinking Focus:** What was the Scientific Revolution?

## New Visions of the Natural World

In the 1500s, scientists like Copernicus questioned the old theories. These theories said that the earth was the center of the universe. Copernicus decided that the sun was the center of the universe. Earth and all of the other planets move in regular circles, called orbits, around the sun. Protestant and Catholic leaders were against this theory. The Catholic church even declared that Copernicus and all people believing in his theory were heretics.

At the same time, Andreas Vesalius made very careful observations of the human body and wrote them in a book. His work questioned the accepted theories about the human body. Both Copernicus and Vesalius looked very closely at the natural world. They were not afraid to question accepted beliefs. Both scientists were leaders in the **Scientific Revolution**. This was a period of new thinking and careful study of the natural world.

[?] How did the scientific discoveries of Copernicus offer a new view on the world?

## Galileo and the Church

Galileo was another scientist who did not accept the old theories. He built the strongest telescope so that he could look at the planets and stars in the sky. He saw the rings around the planet Saturn, Jupiter's moons, and craters on the surface of our moon. Galileo's results agreed with Copernicus's theories. They also showed that the sun was the center of the universe. Galileo argued his ideas in his book, *Dialogue Concerning the Two Chief World Systems*.

**Scientific Revolution**
(sīən-tĭf′ĭk rĕv′ə-lōō′shən)
the era of scientific thought in Europe during which careful observation of the natural world was made and accepted beliefs were questioned

*Summary continues on next page*

Reading Support Resources

The Catholic church was angry with Galileo. The church's teachings had always placed the earth at the center of the universe. The Roman Catholic Inquisition declared that Galileo was a heretic. They placed his book on the list of forbidden books. In court, Galileo declared that he did not believe in Copernicus's theories. But privately, he still believed in a sun-centered universe. He continued his scientific work until he died. By the 1630s, most people accepted the idea of a sun-centered universe.

**?** Why was the Catholic church threatened by Galileo's ideas?

## The Scientific Method

The Scientific Revolution also included philosophers and writers. Francis Bacon was an English philosopher. He wrote a book about how to do scientific research. He said that observation is important. And he said that it is also important to do experiments. His idea became known as the **scientific method.** Bacon said that a scientist must form a **hypothesis,** or an idea, that can be tested with experiments. A scientist can make a conclusion after the hypothesis has been tested.

Sir Isaac Newton, another English scientist, widened many of Galileo's theories. He added to the scientific method by looking at many kinds of information, or data. He got accurate results from all of this data. For example, he questioned the force that makes objects fall to the earth. Could this be the same force that holds the moon and planets in their positions around the sun? Newton described this force as gravity. Today it is accepted that gravity holds the planets and moon in their paths around the sun.

**?** What was revolutionary about the scientific method?

**scientific method**
(sī´ən-tĭf´ĭk mĕth´əd)

a series of logical steps formulated by Francis Bacon and used in scientific research that stressed observation and experimentation

**hypothesis**
(hī-pŏth´ĭ-sĭs)

an assumption that accounts for a set of facts and that can be tested by investigation

# Chapter Overview
## The Age of Exploration

**Fill in the blanks below with information from the chapter.**

## Europe Explores the World

| Travel, Trade, and Exploration | • Advances in geographic knowledge |
| | • Increased trade, demand for goods |
| | • Spreading Christianity |
| | • _____ |

↓

| Adventure and Profit | • _____ |
| | • Preparations for the journey |
| | • _____ |
| | • Commerce and colonies |

↓

| Exploring the Americas | • Christopher Columbus |
| | • _____ |
| | • _____ |

Reading Support Resources

**CHAPTER 14**

# Lesson 1 Preview
## Travel, Trade, and Exploration

*(Across the Centuries pp. 364–370)*

### European Exploration

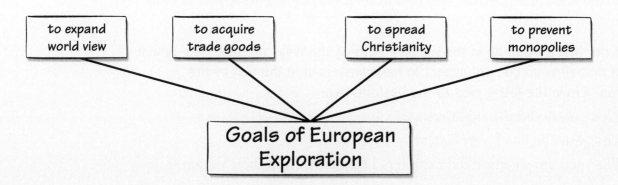

1. **Look at the graphic organizer above. From the information in the organizer, decide whether each statement that follows is true or false. Write *T* or *F* on the line.**

   a. Europeans explored new lands to spread Christianity. ___

   b. Europeans explored to prevent others from having a monopoly. ___

   c. Europeans were interested in acquiring new trade goods. ___

   d. The world view expanded to acquire trade goods. ___

2. **Look at the map on page 366 in your text. By what route were goods from China brought to European markets?**

   _____

   _____

   _____

   _____

   _____

CHAPTER 14

# Lesson 1 Reading Strategy
## Travel, Trade, and Exploration

*(Across the Centuries* pp. 364–370)

**Self-Question** This reading strategy helps you stay focused on what you read. Ask yourself questions before you read a section. Then read to see if you can find the answer to your questions.

1.  **Read the first paragraph in the section "Finding the Way" on page 365. Which question below do you <u>not</u> expect to have answered in the rest of the section? Circle the letter next to the best answer.**

    a.  What routes did the explorers use?

    b.  What was life like for peasants?

    c.  What new information did explorers bring back from their voyages?

2.  **Read the heading "Meeting the Demand for Goods" on page 366 and then look at the map. Write two questions you expect to have answered in the section.**

    _____

    _____

    **Now read the section to see if the questions you wrote were answered. If they were, write the answers to the questions.**

    _____

3.  **Read the section "Searching for New Markets" on pages 369 and 370. Use the questions on the following chart to guide you in your reading. Then fill in the answers to the questions.**

| Ask Yourself | Answers |
| --- | --- |
| a. Why did the Portuguese government often owe a trade debt? | |
| b. Where did Portugal and Spain obtain their gold? | |
| c. What route were explorers looking for? | |

# Lesson 1 Summary
## Travel, Trade, and Exploration

*(Across the Centuries pp. 364–370)*

**Thinking Focus:** Why did travelers in the 1400s risk their lives to explore parts of the world that were unknown to them?

## Finding the Way

With good maps, new knowledge, and a desire to trade, Europeans set out on voyages of exploration. The Crusades had shown many Europeans the wider world and they were eager to trade with other countries. Trips such as Marco Polo's visit to China sparked Europeans' imagination. Other early travelers such as the Arab Ibn Battuta and the Portuguese explorer Vasco da Gama gave mapmakers valuable geographic information. Between the late 1200s and 1500, European geographers began to produce a more accurate picture of the world, including its shape and size. Universities brought advanced learning from Asia and Africa to European towns, including a knowledge of geography, mapmaking, and sailing.

### European Exploration

| Cause | Effect |
|---|---|
| • tales from travelers | • interest in new places |
| • growth of towns and trade | • desire to trade with other countries |
| • translations of books from Africa and Asia | • better knowledge of geography |
| • charts of the coastlines | • safer travel |
| • more accurate maps | • long-distance travel |

[?] What developments between the late 1200s and 1500 spurred European interest in exploring the world?

*Summary continues on next page*

## Meeting the Demand for Goods

In the 1300s and 1400s, Europeans wanted to buy spices, silks, dyes, and gems from the East. Traders carried these goods from Asia over sea and land to port cities on the Mediterranean Sea.

From the Mediterranean ports, Eastern goods were loaded onto Italian ships to be carried to other parts of Europe. The Italian cities of Venice and Genoa grew wealthy from this trade. By the end of the 1300s, Venice had a **monopoly** over trade with the East.

[?]  How did Europeans obtain goods from the East?

## Carrying Christianity Across the Sea

From the 700s on, the Spanish and Portuguese had been fighting against the spread of Islam. These wars had an influence on Spanish and Portuguese exploration. Some explorers wanted to convert people to Christianity in newly explored lands as a way of gaining help in the war against Islam. For this reason, many of the Spanish and Portuguese voyages of exploration took Christian missionaries with them. Others thought they could help non-Christians by making them Christians.

[?]  What role did religion play during the new era of European exploration?

## Searching for New Markets

Portugal bought more goods than it sold. For this reason, the Portuguese government was often in debt to other governments. Portugal had to pay the debts to maintain the **balance of trade.** The other countries wanted the debts paid with gold, which often took the form of **bullion.** In 1419, Portuguese explorers sailed along the west coast of Africa to look for new gold sources. They hoped to avoid paying North African gold traders and deal directly with the gold producers. The Portuguese also looked for a sea route to India and China that would break the Italian monopoly on east-west trade.

[?]  Why did Portugal want to find new markets?

**monopoly**
(mə-nŏp′ə-lē)

one group's total control of the means to produce a service

**balance of trade**
(băl′əns ŭv trād)

the difference in value between the total of goods brought into a nation (imports) and the total of goods sent out of a nation (exports)

**bullion**
(bŏol′yən)

gold or silver in the form of bars of a specific weight

CHAPTER 14

# Lesson 2 Preview
## Adventure and Profit

*(Across the Centuries pp. 371–376)*

### Finding the Sea Route From Europe to Asia

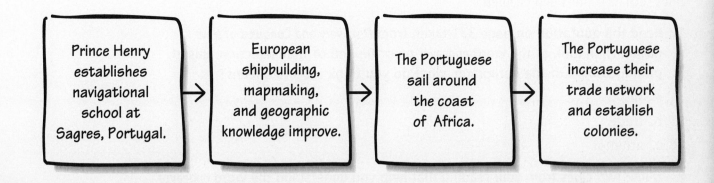

Prince Henry establishes navigational school at Sagres, Portugal. → European shipbuilding, mapmaking, and geographic knowledge improve. → The Portuguese sail around the coast of Africa. → The Portuguese increase their trade network and establish colonies.

1. **Look at the graphic organizer above. Then read the following sentences and fill in the blanks.**

   Prince Henry established a _____ in Portugal. With better

   geographic knowledge and shipbuilding, the Portuguese sailed around the

   coast of _____. The Portuguese established _____
   in order to trade.

2. **Look at the illustration of the caravel on page 373 in your text and read the captions. List three features that make the caravel better than earlier European ships.**

   _____

   _____

   _____

   _____

   _____

   _____

   _____

   _____

# Lesson 2 Reading Strategy
## Adventure and Profit

*(Across the Centuries* pp. 371–376)

**Think About Words** This reading strategy helps you figure out the meaning of new words. When you come to an unfamiliar word, look for word parts you already know and use clues such as context and pictures.

1. Read the quotation on page 371 taken from *Discovery and Conquest of New Guinea.* Then look at the word *endeavor* near the end of that selection. Based on the context of the paragraph, what do you think *endeavor* means?

   a. sail
   b. trade
   c. attempt

2. Name two clues from your reading that help you understand the word *endeavor*.

   _____

3. Look at the pictures on pages 372–373 and read the captions. Then read the section "Preparations for Sailing." Based on the context of the section, what do you think *astrolabe* means? Circle the letter next to the best answer.

   a. wind
   b. temperature
   c. an instrument used to determine latitude

   **Name two clues from your reading that help you understand the word *astrolabe*.**

   _____

4. Read the rest of the section. Choose a word from the section that is new to you. Then fill in as much of the chart below as you can.

   | New word: |
   |---|
   | Clues from reading: |
   | Parts of the word I already know: |
   | Similar words I already know: |
   | The word means: |

# Lesson 2 Summary
## Adventure and Profit

*(Across the Centuries* pp. 371–376)

**Thinking Focus:** How did Prince Henry's center for navigation help establish Portugal's trading empire in the 1500s?

## Prince Henry, Navigator

Prince Henry of Portugal wanted to explore to find the source of African gold. He also hoped to find new markets and goods for Portugal. Henry created a center for learning about navigation and exploration in the city of Sagres, in the south of Portugal. Many scholars, explorers, and mapmakers from faraway places came to work with Henry. Henry financed voyages down the West African coast. When people returned from these travels, the information they brought back helped make better navigational maps.

**?** Why was Prince Henry of Portugal nicknamed "the Navigator"?

## Preparations for Sailing

Henry's experts created or improved instruments to help sailors stay on course. The compass, the astrolabe, and the cross-staff measured latitude, or location north or south of the Earth's equator. Henry's experts designed new mathematical tables to be used with these tools. Sailors then measured the angle of the North Star or the sun against the Earth's horizon. Now, travelers could find their location in open seas with no land in sight.

Prince Henry also developed a new ship called a **caravel**. The caravel could make sharp turns, ride rough seas, and sail into the wind. It was also stronger and quicker than other ships. The caravel became the most popular ship for European voyages in the 1400s and 1500s.

**?** What technological improvements made exploration by sea possible in the 1400s?

**caravel**
(kăr′ə-vĕl′)
a swift sailing ship used by the Spanish and Portuguese in their explorations

*Summary continues on next page*

# The Portuguese Explorations

Prince Henry's ships sailed farther than European ships had ever sailed before. In 1433, a Portuguese ship was the first to sail south of Cape Bojador. Each year after that, Portuguese ships got farther down the coast. They came back with ivory, gold, pepper, and slaves. To trade goods back and forth, Henry set up a trading post on the African coast.

Henry died in 1460. Was there a way to sail directly to India? In 1488, Bartholomeu Dias sailed around the Cape of Good Hope. In 1498, Vasco da Gama sailed around the cape and reached India. There was a sea route to India around Africa.

?  Why did the Portuguese want to explore the west coast of Africa?

# Commerce and Colonies

The Portuguese raised **capital** to pay for these voyages. Then Portuguese people settled in **colonies** in islands off the west coast of Africa. Wheat and sugar were grown there. Sugar was prized in European markets. The Portuguese bought more and more slaves to grow more sugar.

The Portuguese also wanted to stop Arab and Indian traders from using the overland trade routes. They set up trading posts around the Indian Ocean. And they gained control of a large part of the eastern trade for nearly 100 years.

?  How did Portugal profit from the colonies it established off the coast of West Africa?

**capital**
(kăp'ĭ-tl)

money or property used for the production of more wealth

**colony**
(kŏl'ə-nē)

a settlement in a distant land whose citizens keep close ties to their parent country

**CHAPTER 14**

# Lesson 3 Preview
## Exploring the Americas

*(Across the Centuries pp. 377–381)*

### Newcomers to the Americas

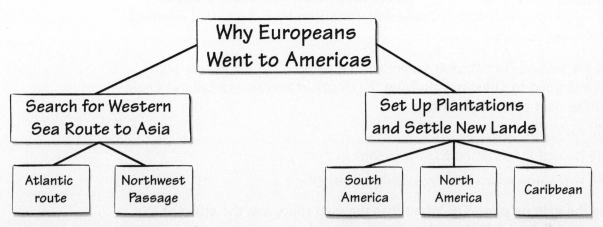

1. **Look at the graphic organizer above. Then read the sentences below. Write *T* next to sentences that are true. Write *F* next to sentences that are false.**

   ____ a.  Europeans went to America to search for the Caribbean.

   ____ b.  Europeans wanted to settle new lands and set up plantations.

   ____ c.  The Northwest Passage was discovered as Europeans were searching for a sea route to Asia.

   ____ d.  Asians settled new lands in South Africa.

2. **Look at the graph on page 379 in your text. Then answer the following questions:**

   a.  In what year was the export of silver and gold from the Americas the greatest?

   _____

   b.  How much gold and silver was shipped in 1570?

   _____

CHAPTER 14

# Lesson 3 Reading Strategy
## Exploring the Americas

(*Across the Centuries* pp. 377–381)

**Cause and Effect** This reading strategy helps you understand events and why they occur. As you read, think about the factors that caused an event. Then think about what the effects of that event may be.

1. Read the section "Christopher Columbus" on pages 377–379 in your text. What event led to Columbus studying the charts of Portuguese sailors? Circle the letter next to the best answer.

   a. He needed money.

   b. He needed information to visit friends in Portugal.

   c. He was shipwrecked off the coast of Portugal.

2. Study the map on page 378. What does the map show was the effect of the voyages of Columbus? Circle the letter next to the best answer.

   a. Other explorers followed Columbus.

   b. European explorations west ended with Columbus.

   c. Magellan decided to travel north on the first part of his voyage.

3. Read the heading "The Spanish in the Americas" on page 379. Then look at the graph. Write one sentence about the cause of new wealth for Spain.

   _____

4. Read the sections "The Spanish in the Americas" and "Europeans in North America" on pages 379–381. Then fill in the chart below.

| Cause | Effect |
|---|---|
| a. | Millions of native inhabitants died of diseases in the early 1500s. |
| b. | Colonists from England, France, and Holland began to arrive in North America. |
| c. | The importance of Mediterranean trade with the Far East declined. |

# Lesson 3 Summary
## Exploring the Americas

*(Across the Centuries* pp. 377–381)

**Thinking Focus:** What role did Christopher Columbus's voyages play in the colonization of North America?

## Christopher Columbus

Columbus was born in Italy around 1451. As a young sailor, he was shipwrecked off the coast of Portugal, and landed near Prince Henry's navigation center. He studied Henry's maps, charts, and books, and dreamed of sailing from Spain to Asia. Instead of sailing to the east, Columbus wanted to sail to the west. He got the King and Queen of Spain to support him.

In 1492, Columbus set sail from Spain for Asia. He had three ships and a crew of 88 men. After two months, Columbus sighted land. He thought that he was off the coast of Japan or China. Later, it was learned that the land was a group of islands in the Caribbean.

[?]  Why did Columbus continue to explore the islands in the Caribbean and the coasts of South and Central America?

## The Spanish in the Americas

The Spanish wanted to protect their rights to American land and seas. The pope agreed to write a treaty between Spain and Portugal. It stated that all the land east of a north-south line drawn through what is now Brazil belonged to Portugal. All land to the west of this point went to Spain. The resulting Treaty of Tordesillas gave most of the Americas to Spain.

Rumors about the riches of the Americas drew Spanish adventurers to these new lands in search of silver and gold. Wherever they found these riches, they killed the native people so they could control the resources.

*Summary continues
on next page*

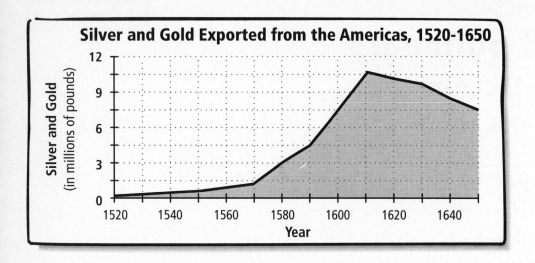

**Silver and Gold Exported from the Americas, 1520–1650**

Spanish colonists set up plantations to grow sugar, tobacco, and other crops for export to Europe. They forced Indians to do the work. These workers were poorly fed, overworked, and beaten. Some of them died. Many more died from diseases brought from Europe. Some Spanish priests tried unsuccessfully to use the laws to protect the Indians.

? Why was it necessary to create laws designed to protect the Indians from the Spanish colonists?

## Europeans in North America

Other European countries began paying for voyages of exploration. English ships first landed in North America in 1497. By the 1600s, the English began to set up colonies in North America. Earlier, in 1513, the Spanish sailor Ferdinand Magellan made the first **circumnavigation** of the Earth. He reported that a huge, unknown continent blocked the western route to Asia. Other explorers wanted to prove that there was a way to sail around or through the continent.

The French sent explorers to North America in search of this route. This route came to be known as the Northwest Passage. During their travels in the northern parts of the continent the French claimed some of the continent as their own. The French, English, and Dutch set up colonies in North America. They cleared land for farms, searched for gold and other minerals, and trapped animals for fur. Many came to seek religious freedom. The importance of Mediterranean trade with the East fell, as sugar plantations in the Caribbean made the Atlantic trade more profitable. Countries with colonies in the New World, such as Holland, England, and France, became the new powers.

? What was the result of France's search for the Northwest Passage?

**circumnavigation**
(sûr´kəm-năv´ĭ-gā´shən)
the act of sailing around the world

# Chapter Overview
## Early American Civilizations

**Fill in the blank spaces below with information from the chapter.**

When:
1800 B.C.–A.D. 1300
Where:
The Americas
Who:
Olmec, Maya, Tiwanakans, and Moche

## Ancient America

### The First Americans

What they hunted: _____

What they farmed: _____

### Olmec

Where: _____
_____
_____
_____
_____

Achievements:
• advanced farming
• sculpture
• art

### Maya

Where: Yucatan
Peninsula region

Achievements:
_____
_____
_____
_____
_____

### Tiwanakans and Moche

Where: _____
_____
_____
_____
_____

Achievements:
• gold-work
• pottery
• adaptations to the land

CHAPTER 15
# Lesson 1 Preview
## Origins

*(Across the Centuries* pp. 396–399)

## Humans Come to the Americas

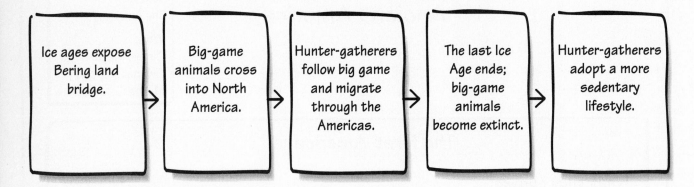

1. **Look at the graphic organizer above. Then read the following paragraph and fill in the blanks.**

   The Ice Ages exposed the _____ land bridge. This allowed big-game animals to cross into _____. People who were hunter-gatherers followed the animals and _____ through the Americas. As the big-game animals became _____, the hunter-gatherers adapted a more _____ lifestyle.

2. **Look at the map on page 398 in your text. What did archaeologists find at both Onion Portage in the north and Fell's Cave in the south?**

   _____

   _____

CHAPTER 15

# Lesson 1 Reading Strategy
## Origins

(*Across the Centuries* pp. 396–399)

**Cause and Effect** This reading strategy helps you understand events and why they occur. As you read, think about the factors that caused an event. Then think about what the effects of that event may be.

1. Read the first two paragraphs in the section "Migrants from Asia" on page 396. What caused the Bering land bridge to become exposed? Circle the letter next to the best answer.

   a. people and animals

   b. glaciers that lowered the level of the ocean

   c. flooding and high winds

2. Read the rest of the section "Migrants from Asia" on page 397. What was one of the effects of the Bering land bridge?

   _____

   _____

3. Read the section "Early Hunter-Gatherers" on pages 397–398. What caused early people to become better hunters?

   _____

   _____

4. Read the section "Early Farmers" on pages 398–399. Fill in the chart below.

| Cause | Effect |
|---|---|
| Big game die out. | Hunter-gatherers _____ _____ |
| Hunter-gatherers _____ | They make baskets, nets, and harpoons. |
| People see that plants grow in the same place every year. | They _____ _____ |

# Lesson 1 Summary
## Origins

(*Across the Centuries* pp. 396–399)

---

**Thinking Focus:** Describe the development of early communities in the Americas.

## Migrants from Asia

The first people to come to the Americas may have been hunters from Asia. Archaeologists have different theories about how these hunters reached North America. One possible route was over a land bridge. Scientists think that during several Ice Ages between 33,000 and 10,000 B.C., ocean water froze into ice. So much water froze that the ocean levels dropped. This exposed a 50-mile stretch of land that connected Siberia in Asia to Alaska in North America. This stretch of land is known as the Bering land bridge. Animals crossed from one side to the other. Hunters soon followed, traveling from Asia to North America. Over thousands of years, people and animals moved farther south. By 10,500 B.C., there were people living in South America. In 1998, archaeologists found evidence that people may have migrated to the Americas by boat. Native American creation tales teach that humans did not come from Asia, but were created in North America.

**?** Describe a migration of Asians to the Americas.

### Bering Land Bridge Theory

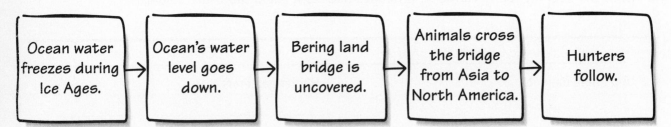

Ocean water freezes during Ice Ages. → Ocean's water level goes down. → Bering land bridge is uncovered. → Animals cross the bridge from Asia to North America. → Hunters follow.

*Summary continues on next page*

Reading Support Resources

# Early Hunter-Gatherers

The hunters who crossed the Bering land bridge made their own weapons and tools. They sharpened pieces of stone and attached them to long wooden spears or animal bones. A group of 20 to 50 hunters could kill big animals such as mastodons, sabre-tooth cats, and bison. They also hunted smaller animals such as deer, foxes, and turkeys. They gathered nuts, berries, and other plant foods. Scholars call these people **hunter-gatherers.**

Many of the large animals died out by 8000 B.C. No one knows why these animals became **extinct.** Some scientists believe that when the climate got warmer, the grassland dried up and the animals ran out of food. Other scientists think the hunters learned better ways of hunting and killed off too many animals.

**?** What did early hunter-gatherers eat, and how did they get their food?

# Early Farmers

The hunter-gatherers had to change their way of life when the big animals died out. They hunted smaller animals and they did not travel so far to hunt. They spent more time in one place and lived a more **sedentary** life. Hunter-gatherers made new tools, such as baskets to store food and harpoons to catch fish. These people learned that they could use seeds to grow food-producing plants. They probably learned that plants grew better in open, sunny places. So they cut down trees and bushes with their stone axes. These hunter-gatherers had become farmers. They built places to live and places for religious activities. Over time, their settlements became villages.

**?** How did hunter-gatherers become food producers?

**hunter-gatherers**
(hŭn´tər-găth´ər-ər)

early people who got food from hunting wild animals and gathering wild plants, roots, nuts, and berries

**extinct**
(ĭk-stĭngkt´)

no longer existing or living

**sedentary**
(sĕd´n-tĕr´ē)

staying in one place and not migrating

Name: _____                    Date: _____

# Lesson 2 Preview
## The Olmec

*(Across the Centuries pp. 400–403)*

### The First Civilization of the Americas

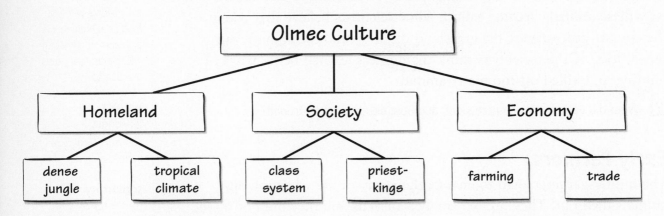

1. **Look at the graphic organizer above. Then read the following sentences and fill in the blanks.**

   a. The land the Olmec lived on was a _____.

   b. How did the Olmec make their living? _____

2. **Look at the photograph and map at the top of page 401 in your text. Which continent lies just to the south of where the Olmec once lived?**

   _____

Reading Support Resources

# Lesson 2 Reading Strategy
## The Olmec

(*Across the Centuries* pp. 400–403)

**Finding the Main Idea** This reading strategy helps you organize and remember what you read. When you finish a selection, jot down the main idea and its supporting details.

1. **Read the section "A Fertile Environment" on page 401. Which sentence below best expresses the main idea of the section?**

   a. The Olmec lived in a dense jungle.

   b. Although the land was a dense swampy jungle, the Olmec were able to find ways of farming.

   c. The Olmec developed a class system, a calendar, and trade routes.

2. **Read the section "Elite and Commoners" on pages 401–402. Which of the following best expresses the main idea of the section?**

   a. Olmec farming methods helped the people build a rich culture.

   b. The Olmec culture was divided into two distinct social classes.

   c. The huge stone heads found at La Venta are probably portraits of Olmec leaders.

3. **Which of the sentences in question 2 is a detail that supports the main idea?**

   _____

   _____

4. **Read the section "Trade and Competition" on page 403. Then fill in the chart below titled "Olmec Trade and Competition."**

| Olmec Trade and Competition | |
|---|---|
| Main idea: | |
| Supporting details: | |

# Lesson 2 Summary
## The Olmec

*(Across the Centuries* pp. 400–403)

**Thinking Focus:** What evidence suggests that the Olmec civilization was complex?

## A Fertile Environment

The Olmec civilization developed around 1200 B.C. in an area between the Gulf of Mexico and the Tuxtla Mountains. The Olmec population grew because the people became efficient producers of food. They learned how to adapt to the yearly floods and dense jungles. Floods deposited fertile soil. Rivers provided fish. Jungle animals could be hunted. The Olmec learned to farm the fast-growing jungle by clearing only small pieces of land at one time.

**?** What environmental factors helped the Olmec develop a complex society?

## Elite and Commoners

Archaeologists use artifacts to reach conclusions about Olmec society. Looking at huge, carved, stone heads, archaeologists concluded that many workers were needed to create and move the monuments to burial sites. The workers were probably directed by a small group of supervisors. Archaeologists believe that there were at least two social classes among the Olmec: the upper, or **elite**, class and the lower class, or commoners. As the population increased, the Olmec developed a class system, trade networks, and rituals that are features of a society.

**?** What do the artifacts found at Olmec burial sites reveal about Olmec society?

**elite**
(ĭ-lēt′)
a small, privileged group
at the top of a society

*Summary continues
on next page*

## Evidence of Olmec Social Classes

| Artifacts | Conclusions |
|---|---|
| Huge Olmec carved heads | Moving the heads would require a division of labor into supervisors and workers. |
| Simple graves, fancy graves | Two types of graves suggest commoners and elite. |

## Power and Religion

Olmec rulers were priest-kings from the elite class. These rulers were religious leaders as well as warriors who protected the village. The Olmec believed in as many as 15 different gods. They thought their priest-kings were related to these gods. The priest-kings were supposed to influence the gods to send good weather for the crops. The Olmec made offerings to please the gods in religious rituals. Sometimes these offerings included the killing of animals or human beings.

[?]  What role did priest-kings play in Olmec society?

## Trade and Competition

Jade was very valuable to the Olmec. Archaeologists think that the Olmec traveled long distances to trade for jade and other raw materials. Artifacts and **hieroglyphs** show that the Olmec traveled up to 500 miles from their homes.

The Olmec fought neighboring tribes and each other for control of materials and trade routes. This fighting might have been what destroyed the Olmec society. Major Olmec settlements were in decline by 400 B.C.

The Olmec culture spread to other cultures in the region. Around 200 B.C., a great city grew in the Valley of Mexico. It was called Teotihuacan. This city had streets, markets, sewers, and water systems and lasted until about A.D. 650. After the city fell, people from the north moved back to the central area. They brought with them a group called the Toltec. These people later came to rule the northern and western parts of the Valley of Mexico.

[?]  How did Olmec competition for goods and trade routes affect their civilization?

**hieroglyph**
(hī′ər-ə-glĭf′)
a writing system that uses pictures instead of words

**CHAPTER 15**

# Lesson 3 Preview
## The Maya

*(Across the Centuries* pp. 404–409)

### The Maya

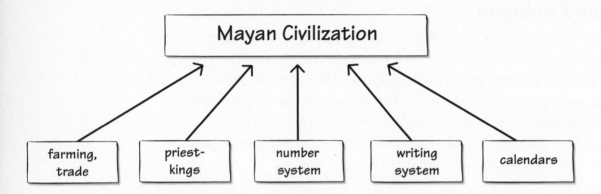

1. **Look at the graphic organizer above. Then read the following sentences and fill in the blanks.**

   a. The Maya were ruled by _____.

   b. The Maya were able to keep track of events by means of their

   _____, _____, and _____.

2. **Look at the map on page 405 in your text. Plan a trip from Uxmal to Palenque, then to Copán, and then back to Uxmal. If you could travel in a straight line, what would be the distances of the three parts of your journey?**

   _____

   _____

   _____

   _____

   _____

   _____

   _____

   _____

   _____

CHAPTER 15

# Lesson 3 Reading Strategy
## The Maya

(*Across the Centuries* pp. 404–409)

**Using the Visuals** This reading strategy helps you use photographs, maps, charts, and illustrations to help you understand what you read. As you read, be sure to study the visuals and carefully read the captions.

1. **Look at the timeline at the top of page 404. According to the timeline, how long did the Mayan civilization last? Circle the letter next to the best answer.**

   a. 1,800 years

   b. 2,700 years

   c. 4,000 years

2. **Look at the map on page 405. Where are the marshlands located? Circle the letter next to the best answer.**

   a. along the Gulf of Mexico and Caribbean Sea coastlines

   b. in the southern area

   c. at the northern tip of the Yucatan Peninsula

3. **Look at the pictures on page 406 and read the captions. Explain how the Maya brought water to their terraced fields.**

   _____

   _____

   _____

4. **Look at the soil diagram at the bottom of page 406. Then, put the soil layers in the correct order from 1 (the bottom layer) to 5 (the top layer).**

   ____ smooth gravel

   ____ clay

   ____ topsoil

   ____ cobblestone

   ____ coarse gravel

# Lesson 3 Summary
## The Maya

*(Across the Centuries* pp. 404–409)

**Thinking Focus:** In what ways were the Maya an advanced civilization?

## A Growing Civilization

The people known as the Maya settled in an area of mountains and valleys. The Maya were spread out over 125,000 square miles. Archaeologists think the Maya began working the land as early as 1800 B.C. They built small farming villages. By A.D. 200, some of these villages grew into cities.

Mayan cities were built around religious centers. Some cities had great palaces. The Maya built flat-topped pyramids made of limestone. At the top of these pyramids were temples. That was where the Mayan priest-kings held religious rituals.

? What were Mayan cities like?

## An Economy Based on Agriculture

As Mayan cities grew, farmers needed to produce more food. They found ways to farm places they had not farmed before. They farmed the sides of hills. They built raised fields in the wet lowlands. In heavy forests, they burned trees and other plants to clear the land for farming. They moved good soil to areas that had poor soil. They dug water systems to bring water to dry areas. They used all these methods to grow crops such as corn, beans, and squash.

Eventually, the Maya grew more food than they needed. They traded their food with other people living in Central America and Mexico. In return, they got things they couldn't produce themselves, such as jade, feathers, and cacao beans.

? What techniques enabled highland and lowland farmers to become more efficient?

*Summary continues on next page*

## Priests as Kings

The Maya worshipped many gods. They also worshipped their rulers. They thought their rulers could influence the gods. The Maya told stories of their rulers in hieroglyphs. These picture symbols were carved into stone columns called **steles**. One of the rulers was Pacal. He ruled the Maya for 68 years. Like other Maya rulers he was a priest as well as a warrior. Priest-kings like Pacal killed animals and sometimes people as offerings to the gods.

**?** What do we know about Mayan rulers?

## Mayan Achievements

The Maya created their own number system based on the number 20. They also used hieroglyphs. Each picture stood for a sound. Some hieroglyphs stood for whole ideas, such as life or happiness. The Mayan priest-kings used hieroglyphs in their written records. Each record book is called a **codex**. Archaeologists have learned much about the Maya from these books. For example, they know that the Maya had two calendars. The calendars were based on the movements of the sun, moon, and stars. The Maya used the calendars to plan and record their years. The Maya also were artists and skilled builders of elaborate cities.

**?** Describe the Mayan writing and number systems.

**stele**
(stē′lē)
a stone column with hieroglyphs carved into it

**codex**
(kō′dĕks′)
a record book kept by early people in Central America, such as the Maya

CHAPTER 15

# Lesson 4 Preview
## The Tiwanakans and the Moche

(*Across the Centuries* pp. 412–415)

### Two South American Cultures

|  | Tiwanakans | Moche |
|---|---|---|
| **Homeland** | cold, high plateau | dry, desert coast |
| **Farming** | irrigation canals, raised soil beds | aqueducts, terraced fields |
| **Lifestyle** | social classes, honored the condor | social classes, worshiped many gods |
| **Fate** | abandoned city of Tiwanaku by 1300 | abandoned city of Moche by about 600 |

1. **Look at the graphic organizer above. Then read the following sentences and fill in the blanks.**

   a. What were the differences between where the Tiwanakans lived and where the Moche lived?

   _____

   _____

   _____

   b. How many years was it from when the Moche abandoned their city to when the Tiwanakans abandoned theirs?

   _____

2. **Look at the small square map at the bottom of page 412. What mountain range separated Moche from Tiwanaku?**

   _____

CHAPTER 15

# Lesson 4 Reading Strategy
## The Tiwanakans and the Moche

(*Across the Centuries* pp. 412–415)

**Predict/Infer** This reading strategy helps you understand what you have read and what you will read next. Before you read a section, think about the titles, pictures, and captions. Then think about what will happen in the selection.

1. **Look at the pictures and map on pages 412–415. Fill out the chart below with your inferences about the Tiwanakans and the Moche.**

| Tiwanakan Environment and Culture | Moche Environment and Culture |
|---|---|
|  |  |
|  |  |
|  |  |

2. **Read the lesson title and the first two paragraphs on page 412. What do you predict will be the subject described in the rest of the page?**

_____

_____

3. **Read from the heading "Living and Working" on page 414 through the first paragraph of the blue heading "Tiwanakan Lifestyle." What do you predict will be the result of the Tiwanakans building roads?**

_____

_____

4. **Look at the picture of the gold condor at the top of page 415 and read the caption. What can you infer about the Tiwanakan religion?**

_____

_____

CHAPTER 15
# Lesson 4 Summary
## The Tiwanakans and the Moche

(*Across the Centuries* pp. 412–415)

**Thinking Focus:** In what ways did the Tiwanakans and Moche adapt to the land?

## Adapting to the Land

Tiwanakan culture reached its height from about 300 B.C. to A.D. 1200. When their population was at its largest, the Tiwanakans lived on 1,500 square miles. Their lands stretched from the **altiplano** of Peru and Bolivia down the coast of Peru and into northern Chile. About 400 years after the Tiwanakan culture began, another culture grew up on the northern coast of Peru. These people were called the Moche. They lived in the low hills, river valleys, and dry desert coast near the Andes. Both cultures had to find ways to farm the harsh land they lived on.

Tiwanakan farmers used canals to bring water from lakes to the fields. They led the water into channels between raised growing beds. To create these beds they used a base of stones. Then they added layers of clay and gravel. They topped the whole thing with a layer of rich soil. In this new, better soil Tiwanakans grew potatoes, grains, and other crops. The canals around the beds watered the plants and protected them from frost.

Moche farmers used long aqueducts, or channels, built of mud to bring water to fields. One of these aqueducts was 70 miles long. The Moche also grew crops on the sides of hills. They terraced the steep hill slopes into steps like a giant staircase. In these terraced fields, they grew corn, beans, peanuts, and peppers.

? Describe the methods the Tiwanakans and Moche used to bring water to their farmlands.

**altiplano**
(äl´tĭ-plä´nō)
the land on a high, flat plateau in South America

*Summary continues
on next page*

# Living and Working

Because of their successful farming methods, the populations of both Tiwanakans and Moche increased. Soon social classes began to form. Among the Tiwanakans, the common people did the hard work. They paid two kinds of taxes to the government. Part of the food they grew went to the state. They also spent time each year working for the state. The women usually wove cloth and the men worked the fields and built roads.

Roads were important to Tiwanakan trade. Llama caravans connected the Tiwanakans with parts of Chile and Peru, as well as the jungles of Bolivia. The government encouraged trade by supplying the llamas for the caravans and protecting the roads from attack.

The city of Tiwanaku was a center for trade and religion. Tiwanakans honored the condor and thought their rulers could influence the gods.

The Moche, like the Tiwanakans, made the common people do the hard work. They dug the aqueducts and built the **adobe** pyramids and temples in the ancient city of Moche. The elite class were the artisans, warriors, engineers, and priests.

The tombs of the elite "Lords of Sipan" are the richest tombs found in the Americas. Moche pottery from the tombs show scenes of war and glorious rulers, as well as pictures of daily activities such as farming, weaving, and the worship of many gods.

**adobe**
(ə-dō′bē)
bricks made of mud and straw

? Compare and contrast Tiwanakan and Moche lifestyles.

## Tiwanakan and Moche Farming

| Tiwanakan Farming | Moche Farming |
|---|---|
| used canals | used aqueducts |
| built raised soil beds | farmed on hillsides |
| grew potatoes and grain | grew corn, beans, peanuts, peppers |

# Chapter Overview
## Two American Empires

**CHAPTER 16**

Fill in the blank spaces below with information from the chapter.

**When:**
1230–1572

**Where:**
Central and
South America

**Who:**
The Aztec, Inca,
and Spanish

## The End of an Era

### Aztec

**Where:**  Valley of Mexico

**Achievements:** _____
_____
_____
_____
_____

### Inca

**Where:**  Andes Mountains in Peru,
Bolivia, Ecuador, and Chile

**Achievements:** _____
_____
_____
_____
_____

### The Empires Fall

**Events:**  Spanish arrive; battle for Tenochtitlan; battle at Cajamarca;
march on Cuzco

**Leaders:** _____
_____

## CHAPTER 16
# Lesson 1 Preview
## The Aztec

*(Across the Centuries pp. 422–428)*

### The Aztec Empire

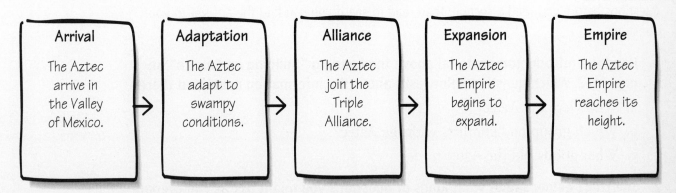

**Arrival** — The Aztec arrive in the Valley of Mexico.

**Adaptation** — The Aztec adapt to swampy conditions.

**Alliance** — The Aztec join the Triple Alliance.

**Expansion** — The Aztec Empire begins to expand.

**Empire** — The Aztec Empire reaches its height.

1. **Look at the graphic organizer above. Circle the letter of the correct statement below.**

    a. The Aztec find it difficult to adapt to the swampy conditions in the Valley of Mexico.

    b. The Aztec Empire is unable to expand because of the swampy conditions.

    c. The Aztec Empire expands and reaches its height after its people join the Triple Alliance.

2. **Look at the map on page 423 in your text. What lake is in the center of the area of the Aztec Empire that expanded between the years 1427 and 1440?**

    _____

CHAPTER 16

# Lesson 1 Reading Strategy
## The Aztec

*(Across the Centuries pp. 422–428)*

**Self-Question** This reading strategy helps you stay focused on what you read. Ask yourself questions before you read a section. Then read to see if you can find the answer to your questions.

1. **Read the introductory material above the heading "Building an Empire" on page 422. Which question below asks about the information contained there?**

   a. Who were the Aztec?

   b. Which group had conflicts with the Aztec?

   c. What goods did the Aztec trade?

2. **The chart below shows what kinds of questions you might ask as you prepare to read the section "Building an Empire" on pages 422–424. As you read that section, look for the answers to the following questions and fill in the chart.**

   a. Where was the empire?

   _____

   b. How did the empire become powerful?

   _____

   c. Who ruled the empire?

3. **Read the heading "Living in the Empire" and the smaller headings that follow on pages 425–427. Which question below would you expect to have answered by reading these pages? Circle the letter next to the best answer.**

   a. What were Aztec markets like?

   b. What is life like in Mexico today?

   c. Where did the Aztec come from?

   **Read the section to see if the question you chose was answered. If it was, write the answer to the question.**

   _____

   _____

# Lesson 1 Summary
## The Aztec

*(Across the Centuries pp. 422–428)*

---

**Thinking Focus:** What methods did the Aztec use to build their large empire?

## Building an Empire

The Aztec empire started on an island in the Valley of Mexico in the early 1300s. Because powerful tribes were already living in the area and had claimed the best farmland, the Aztec had to settle on a small swampy island. They learned to make the best of their surroundings. They used reeds and mud to build huts. They caught and ate birds and fish. The settlers made "floating gardens" called **chinampas**. In these gardens, the Aztec grew corn, beans, peppers, and tomatoes.

The Aztec became famous as skilled fighters. In 1428, the Aztec formed an **alliance** with two powerful tribes. This alliance greatly increased Aztec power. They began to build a large empire. Powerful rulers led Aztec armies into surrounding lands that became part of the Aztec Empire. In 1520, under the ruler Moctezuma, the empire had a population of about 25 million.

**?** How did the Aztec adapt to their swampy environment?

## Living in the Empire

The Aztec divided their society into four social classes: nobles, commoners, serfs, and slaves. Families of the different social classes lived in large settlements called **calpullis** and shared its land. Commoners made up the largest class. The men farmed their own land but also had to farm the nobles' land. The women cooked, wove cloth, and took care of children. Commoners had to pay **tribute** to the government. Tribute could be paid with crops or handmade items like jewelry or clothes. It could also be paid by working on government projects such as temples, canals, or dams.

Like commoners, serfs were farmers. But they could not own the land they farmed. At the bottom of the Aztec social order were the slaves. Many slaves were people from tribes that had been conquered, or defeated, in war. The conquered people had to give up much of their food as tribute and resented Aztec rule.

**chinampas**
(chĭ-năm´pə)

narrow strips of swampy land about 300 feet long and 30 feet wide; the Aztec of Central America used these "floating gardens" for farming

**alliance**
(ə-lī´əns)

an agreement to work together made between groups who have a common goal

**calpulli**
(kăl-pōō´lē)

an Aztec settlement in which families of different social classes lived and shared the land

**tribute**
(trĭb´yōot)

a kind of tax paid with crops, handmade goods, or services to the government

*Summary continues on next page*

The nobles were the smallest class but they were at the top of the Aztec social ladder. Nobles served in the government and as priests and soldiers. They lived off tribute paid by commoners and the conquered peoples who made up a large part of the empire.

**?** Describe the different classes in Aztec society and the effect that tribute had on each of them.

## Fighting for the Gods

The everyday lives of the Aztec were influenced by their religion. Aztec priests offered sacrifices to the gods to bring good harvests. Human sacrifice was common. Some experts think that one of the reasons the Aztec captured people in battle was to frighten their enemies by sacrificing the captives. Aztec soldiers believed that the gods would reward them for their success in battle. The more people they captured, the higher their rank. Aztec soldiers fought without fear of death. They believed their deaths would help the gods to keep the world going.

**?** How were war and religion linked in Aztec culture?

CHAPTER 16

# Lesson 2 Preview
## The Inca

*(Across the Centuries* pp. 429–435)

### The Success of the Inca Empire

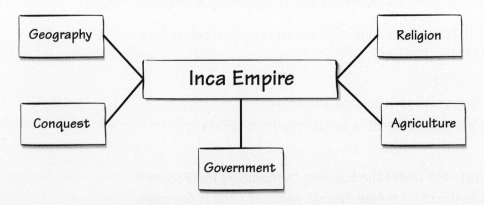

1. **Look at the graphic organizer above. Use the following words to fill in the blanks below.**

| religion | geography | agriculture | Inca |
|---|---|---|---|

a. The _____ Empire was very large and powerful.

b. The _____ of the Inca Empire was made up of mountains, valleys, and rivers.

c. Praying to ancestors was part of Inca _____.

d. The Inca used special methods of _____ that helped them grow abundant crops.

2. **Look at the photograph of the rope bridge at the top of page 432 in your text. Then read the caption. Find another picture in this lesson that shows an Inca technique that is still used today. Write the page number and explain your choice.**

_____

_____

_____

**CHAPTER 16**
# Lesson 2 Reading Strategy
## The Inca
*(Across the Centuries* pp. 429–435)

**Finding the Main Idea** This reading strategy helps you organize and remember what you read. When you finish a selection, jot down the main idea and its supporting details.

1. Read the section "Rising to Power" on page 430. Which sentence below best expresses the main idea of the selection?

   a. The Inca had no writing system.

   b. The Inca called their powerful empire Tihuantinsuyu.

   c. By defeating other tribes in surrounding lands, the Inca built a huge empire.

2. Read the text on pages 431–432 under the heading "Organizing the People." Then read the sentences in the chart below. Decide whether each is the main idea or a supporting detail. Write a *D* next to a supporting detail and an *M* next to the main idea.

| | |
|---|---|
| Nobles lived off tribute and worked as government officials. | |
| A strict social structure helped the Inca ruler keep control over the people. | |
| Most of the people in the empire were commoners. | |

3. Read the text on pages 432–433 under the heading "Working the Land." Then write the main idea below.

   _____

   _____

   **Now write two details that support the main idea.**

   _____

   _____

4. Read the section "Praying to the Ancestors" on pages 433–435. Which sentence best expresses the main idea of the selection?

   a. The Inca believed that dead ancestors and gods looked after them.

   b. The Inca burned sacrifices to the gods.

   c. The Inca believed in life after death.

# Lesson 2 Summary
## The Inca

(*Across the Centuries* pp. 429–435)

---

**Thinking Focus:** In what ways were the Inca a technologically advanced civilization?

## Rising to Power

The Inca competed with other tribes for control of the fertile Cuzco Valley in what is now southern Peru. In 1230, they held only a small amount of land. By 1525, the Inca Empire covered most of what is now Ecuador, Peru, and Bolivia and parts of Argentina and Chile.

**?** What was the extent of the Inca Empire?

## Conquering and Controlling

The Inca had a number of ways of controlling the peoples of their empire. They forced conquered men to join their army and rewarded them for doing well in battle. The Inca posted soldiers throughout their empire. This meant that there was always an army nearby to stop a rebellion. To unite the empire, the Inca made defeated tribes follow the Inca religion and learn the Inca language, Quechua.

Inca society was made up of two classes—nobles and commoners. The commoners' lives were under the complete control of the ruler. Commoners worked very hard in the fields. They also worked on public projects like the building of a complex network of roads, bridges, and tunnels that crossed the Inca Empire.

**?** What methods did the Inca use to control their empire?

## Working the Land

Once the Inca conquered a region, they took total control of the land. Then they divided the farmland into three parts. The commoners harvested one part for the government workers, one part for religious leaders, and one part for themselves.

*Summary continues on next page*

The farmland varied greatly in the different regions of the empire. Some valleys were as high as 8,000 feet above sea level. But others were only a few hundred feet above sea level. In low valleys farmers grew corn (maize), beans, and squash. In the mountains, they raised llamas and alpacas for wool and meat. This way of using land is called a **vertical economy**.

The Inca were able to grow enough food to eat and enough to store by using highly productive farming techniques. One of these techniques was **terrace farming**. Because the soil on mountains was thin, the Inca carried rich topsoil from lower areas to the mountains. They packed it into narrow strips of land called terraces. The terraces went up the mountain like a set of stairs. They also built irrigation systems in case of drought.

[?]  Why was Inca agriculture so productive?

**vertical economy**
(vûr´tǐ-kəl ǐ-kŏn´ə-mē)
the growing of crops and raising of animals according to the elevation, or height, of the land

**terrace farming**
(tĕr´ĭs fär´mǐng)
the building of steps or raised banks of earth so that farming can be done on steep land

# Praying to the Ancestors

To make sure their crops would grow well, the Inca prayed to their gods and ancestors. They believed that there was life after death and that dead rulers, especially, played a role in controlling the future of the empire.

When an Inca ruler died, he was made into a mummy. A mummy is a preserved body. Mummies were brought out for important ceremonies during planting and harvest seasons. The Inca believed that the mummies spoke to living people and to each other through the priests. Inca rulers often based their decisions on the predictions of the priests.

[?]  Why were mummies important to the Inca?

CHAPTER 16

# Lesson 3 Preview
## The Arrival of the Spanish

*(Across the Centuries pp. 437–442)*

### Clash in the Americas

|  | Aztec | Inca | Spanish |
|---|---|---|---|
| **Internal Condition** | civil war | civil war | not applicable |
| **External Condition** | Spanish invade | Spanish invade | not applicable |
| **Impact of Disease** | enormous | enormous | minimal |
| **Weapons** | bows, arrows, clubs | bows, arrows, clubs | guns and cannons |

1. **Look at the graphic organizer above. Then read the following sentences and fill in the blanks.**

   a. The Spanish had weapons, such as guns and _____.

   b. The Inca had weapons, such as _____, arrows, and clubs.

   c. The impact of disease on the _____ was minimal.

   d. The impact of disease on the Aztec was _____.

2. **Read the lesson title and the red and blue headings in your text, pages 437–442. Use words from those headings to fill in the lesson outline below.**

   The Arrival of the Spanish

       **I.** The Empires Weaken

      **II.** Old and New _____ Clash

         **A.** Cortés Conquers the _____

         **B.** _____ Conquers the Inca

     **III.** Two _____ Destroyed

CHAPTER 16

# Lesson 3 Reading Strategy
## The Arrival of the Spanish

(*Across the Centuries* pp. 437–442)

**Compare and Contrast** This reading strategy helps you understand how events are similar and different. As you read about historical events, think about how they compare and contrast with events you already know.

1. **Read the section "The Empires Weaken" on page 438. What situations facing the Inca and the Aztec were similar? Circle the letter next to the best answer.**

   a. Two brothers were fighting for control of the empire.

   b. They were both fighting civil wars.

   c. Francisco Pizarro arrived in both empires.

2. **Read the section "Old and New Worlds Clash" on pages 438–440. Write a sentence about how the Aztec reacted to the arrival of the Spanish. Then write one sentence about how the Inca reacted to the arrival of the Spanish.**

   Aztec _____

   Inca _____

3. **Write a sentence or two comparing and contrasting the Aztecs' and the Incas' reaction to the Spanish.**

   _____

   _____

4. **Read the section "Two Empires Destroyed" on pages 440–442. Compare and contrast the Aztec with the Spanish by filling in the chart below.**

|                  | Spanish | Aztec |
| ---------------- | ------- | ----- |
| Weapons          |         |       |
| Culture/Religion |         |       |
| Way of Fighting  |         |       |

# Lesson 3 Summary
## The Arrival of the Spanish

*(Across the Centuries pp. 437–442)*

**Thinking Focus:** Why were the Spanish able to take over the Aztec and Inca empires so quickly?

## The Empires Weaken

The Spanish **conquistadors** came to the lands of the Aztec and the Inca in the 1500s. At that time, both the Aztec and the Inca were suffering from **civil wars**, food shortages, and the high cost of the wars.

In the Aztec Empire, a number of conquered tribes rebelled against the harshness of Aztec rule. The Aztec ruler Moctezuma sent his armies to many parts of the empire to fight the rebels. Fighting so many battles drained Moctezuma's resources.

When the Spanish arrived in Inca lands in 1532, the Inca Empire was divided. The ruler had died. His two sons, Huascar and Atahualpa, were fighting for the throne. The northern half of the empire supported Atahualpa. The southern half supported Huascar. After three years of civil war, Atahualpa won. But the Inca Empire was greatly weakened.

**conquistador**
(kŏn-kē′stə-dôr′)

the Spanish word for conqueror; usually refers to the Spaniards who came to Latin America in search of riches during the 1500s

**civil war**
(sĭv′əl wôr)

a war between regions or groups of people within one country

[?] How were the internal problems of the Aztec and Inca empires similar, and how did they contribute to their downfall?

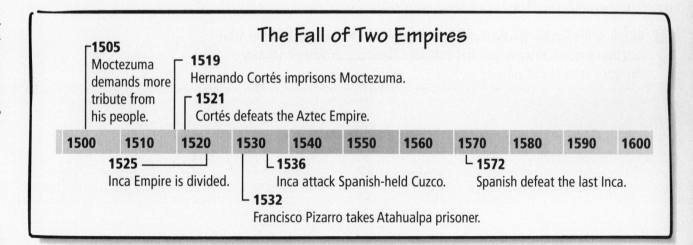

### The Fall of Two Empires

- **1505** Moctezuma demands more tribute from his people.
- **1519** Hernando Cortés imprisons Moctezuma.
- **1521** Cortés defeats the Aztec Empire.

| 1500 | 1510 | 1520 | 1530 | 1540 | 1550 | 1560 | 1570 | 1580 | 1590 | 1600 |

- **1525** Inca Empire is divided.
- **1536** Inca attack Spanish-held Cuzco.
- **1572** Spanish defeat the last Inca.
- **1532** Francisco Pizarro takes Atahualpa prisoner.

## Old and New Worlds Clash

When Moctezuma learned of the arrival of the Spanish leader Hernando Cortés, he welcomed him. Moctezuma thought Cortés might be the Aztec god Quetzalcoatl returning to his country. Within days, Cortés took Moctezuma prisoner. The Spanish persuaded tribes who were against Aztec rule to help them fight the Aztec. The Spanish and this army of rebel tribes surrounded the Aztec capital and cut off its food supplies. On August 13, 1521, with most of their soldiers dead from wounds, disease, or starvation, the Aztec gave up.

The Spanish conquistador Francisco Pizarro arrived in Inca lands in 1532. The Spanish said they only wanted to admire the empire. Atahualpa cautiously allowed the Spanish to enter deep into his empire. Pizarro ordered his army to attack. They killed 5,000 Inca and took Atahualpa prisoner. An army of 200,000 Inca continued to fight the Spanish takeover. But in 1572, the Spanish completely defeated them.

**?** How did the Aztec and Inca rulers receive the Spanish conquistadors?

## Two Empires Destroyed

There are a number of reasons why the Spanish defeated the Aztec and Inca empires so quickly. First, the Spanish had better weapons. Second, the Spanish and the Aztec had very different cultures and beliefs. The Spanish saw the Aztecs as non-Christians who had to be destroyed. The Aztecs thought Cortés might be a god. The Aztecs also fought to take prisoners, but the Spanish fought to kill. Third, the Spanish were helped by the civil wars in both the Inca and Aztec empires. Finally, diseases brought from Europe by the Spanish spread quickly through the Aztec and Inca empires.

**?** Which of the following contributed most significantly to the defeat of the Aztec and Inca empires: disease, civil war, cultural differences, or Spanish military strength? Defend your answer.

# Chapter Overview
## European Rule and Expansion

**Fill in the blank spaces below with information from the chapter.**

**When:**
1400–1763

**Who:**
The French, the English and others

### European Power Grows

**French Monarchy**

• Henry of Navarre

• Louis XIII

• _____

European Rule and Expansion

**English Monarchy**

• Elizabeth I

• Charles I

• William and
  _____

**European Empires**

• Portuguese

• _____

• Dutch

• _____

• _____

**CHAPTER 17**

# Lesson 1 Preview
## The French Monarchy

*(Across the Centuries* pp. 452–456)

### The French Monarchy Builds Absolute Power

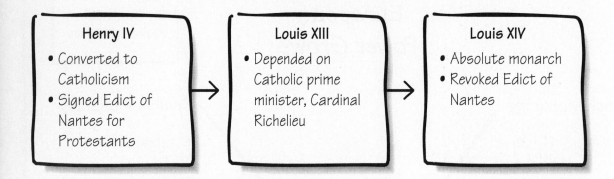

**Henry IV**
- Converted to Catholicism
- Signed Edict of Nantes for Protestants

**Louis XIII**
- Depended on Catholic prime minister, Cardinal Richelieu

**Louis XIV**
- Absolute monarch
- Revoked Edict of Nantes

1. **Look at the graphic organizer above. Then read and answer the following questions:**

   **a.** Who was an absolute monarch?

   _____

   **b.** Who converted to Catholicism?

   _____

   **c.** What was the name of the Catholic prime minister?

   _____

2. **Look at the illustration and its caption on page 453 in your text. What did the Edict of Nantes allow Protestants such as the Huguenots of Lyon to do?**

   _____

   _____

# Lesson 1 Reading Strategy
## The French Monarchy

*(Across the Centuries pp. 452–456)*

**Summarize** This reading strategy helps you remember key points about what you have read. When you get to a good break in your reading, stop and write down the main ideas of what you have read.

1. Read the section "Religious Wars Divide France" on page 453. What is the best summary of the religious issues facing France in the 1500s? Circle the letter next to the best answer.

   a. Henry IV converted to Catholicism twice.

   b. The Edict of Nantes gave Protestants the same civil rights as Catholics.

   c. There was a struggle for power between Protestants and Catholics.

2. Read the section "Cardinal Richelieu Builds the Monarchy" on pages 453–454. Then decide which sentence below is a key point regarding Cardinal Richelieu's goals for the monarchy.

   a. Cardinal Richelieu was the prime minister.

   b. Cardinal Richelieu wanted the king to be the unchallenged ruler of France.

   c. Cardinal Richelieu took away the Huguenots' weapons.

   d. Cardinal Richelieu let the Huguenots practice their religion.

3. Read the section "Nobles and Huguenots" on pages 454–456. Write a summary of Louis XIV's method for keeping the nobles from challenging his power.

   _____

   _____

   _____

4. Read the section "Peasants" on page 456. Write a summary of the problem that faced France's peasants.

   _____

   _____

   _____

# Lesson 1 Summary
## The French Monarchy

*(Across the Centuries* pp. 452–456)

Summary also on Audiotape

**Thinking Focus:** What part did religion play in French history?

## Religious Wars Divide France

Since the Reformation began in 1517, Christians had a choice of being Protestant or Catholic. In France, a small but fast-growing group of French Protestants was known as the Huguenots. The Huguenots and the Catholics struggled for power. The Catholics were in power, but some Catholics feared that the Huguenots would take control of the government. In 1572, the Catholic king of France, Charles IX, and some nobles planned to kill a Huguenot leader. They hoped this would weaken the Huguenots. The plot was discovered. The nobles then spread rumors that the Huguenots wanted revenge against the Catholics. The Catholics responded to the rumors by murdering some 20,000 Huguenots.

The Catholics and Huguenots continued to fight bitterly. In 1589, the French king died. Henry of Navarre was named to become the new king of France. But Henry was a Huguenot. French Catholics refused to let a Protestant rule. Henry converted to Catholicism and was crowned Henry IV of France. In 1598, however, Henry IV met with Protestant leaders in Nantes, France. They created a document called an edict, or order. The Edict of Nantes gave Protestants religious freedom. In 1610, Henry IV was killed by someone who disagreed with the edict.

**[?]** Why did Henry IV issue the Edict of Nantes?

*Summary continues on next page*

# Cardinal Richelieu Builds the Monarchy

When Henry IV was killed, his son, Louis XIII, was only nine years old. Advisers helped him rule. By 1624, Cardinal Richelieu had become Louis's chief adviser, or **prime minister**, and he ruled France for Louis XIII. His goals were to make the king the supreme ruler of France.

Richelieu did not want the nobles to share power with the king. He felt that the nobility might use their castles as centers of power, so he ordered the army to destroy many of the nobles' castles.

[?] Why did Richelieu want to limit the nobles' power?

# Louis XIV Reigns Supreme

Louis XIII died in 1643, and his son, Louis XIV, became king. He was only four years old. For 18 years, Louis XIV was advised by the prime minister, Cardinal Mazarin. When Mazarin died, Louis XIV said that he would rule without a prime minister.

Louis XIV was an **absolute monarch**, an all-powerful ruler. He said that he ruled by **divine right**. Louis made sure that no groups of people would challenge his absolute power. He limited the power of the nobles by inviting them to live with him in his grand palace at Versailles. At Versailles, he was able to keep a close watch on them.

In 1685, Louis got rid of the Edict of Nantes. Without the Edict of Nantes, it was illegal to be a Protestant in France.

**prime minister**
(prīm mĭn´ĭ-stər)
the most important government official who is chosen by a ruler

**absolute monarch**
(ăb´sə-loōt´ mŏn´ərk´)
a ruler who has no limitations of any kind on his or her power

**divine right**
(dĭ-vīn´ rīt)
the right of a ruler to rule, based on the belief that the right comes directly from God and that the ruler is responsible only to God

## Louis XIV's Path to Absolute Power

**Eliminates the Prime Minister**
Louis XIV announces he will rule without a prime minister.

**Weakens the Nobility**
Louis invites French nobles to live with him at Versailles so he can keep a close watch on their activities.

**Bans the Protestants**
Louis revokes the Edict of Nantes, making it illegal to be a Protestant. Many Protestants leave France.

[?] In what ways did Louis XIV govern as an absolute monarch?

**CHAPTER 17**

# Lesson 2 Preview
## The English Monarchy

*(Across the Centuries* pp. 458–463)

## Government in England

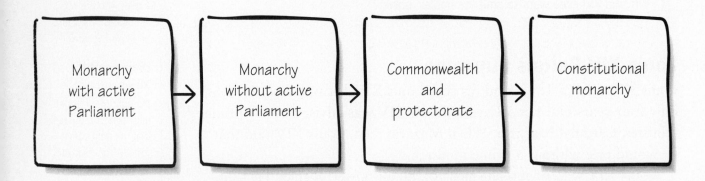

1. **Look at the graphic organizer above. Then read the sentences below. Place the sentences in order according to which happened first, second, third, and fourth.**

   ___ The Commonwealth and then the protectorate are established.

   ___ A Constitutional monarchy is established.

   ___ The monarchy rules without the participation of Parliament.

   ___ The monarchy rules with the participation of Parliament.

2. **Read the time line "English Kings during the Reign of Louis XIV" on pages 462–463 in your text. Write the name of the ruler who reigned after Charles II. How many years did this ruler reign?**

   _____

   _____

   _____

   _____

   _____

   _____

   _____

   _____

CHAPTER 17

# Lesson 2 Reading Strategy
## The English Monarchy

(*Across the Centuries* pp. 458–463)

**Sequence** This reading strategy helps you follow the order of events. As you read, pay attention to dates and times, as well as to words such as *before, finally, after,* and *then.*

1. Read the section "The Church of England" on page 459. Place the following monarchs in order in which they reigned by writing 1, 2, and 3 in the blanks.

   ___ Elizabeth I

   ___ Mary I

   ___ Henry VIII

2. Read from the beginning of the section "The Spanish Armada" on page 459 to the end of the section "The Power of Parliament" on page 460. Place the events listed below in order by writing 1, 2, 3, and 4 in the blanks.

   ___ The Spanish Armada enters the English Channel.

   ___ The English send fire ships toward the Spanish Armada.

   ___ Elizabeth asks Parliament for funds to fight the Spanish Armada.

   ___ The *Magna Carta* is accepted.

3. Read the section "The English Civil War" on pages 460–462. Complete the timeline below with the dates and events surrounding the Civil War.

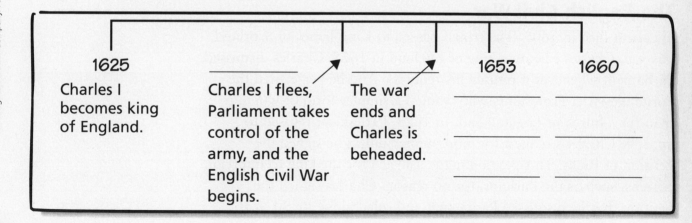

Summary also on
Audiotape

# Lesson 2 Summary
## The English Monarchy

(*Across the Centuries* pp. 458–463)

**Thinking Focus:** What events led to Parliament's becoming a major power in the English government?

## The Reign of Elizabeth I

When Elizabeth I became queen of England in 1558, her country was divided over the issue of religion. Elizabeth's father, Henry VIII, had broken away from the pope's Catholic church and started an English church. Elizabeth was a Protestant. When she became queen, she made the Church of England the nation's official religion.

In the 1580s, Elizabeth supported the Dutch Protestants in their war against Catholic Spain. The Spanish sent an armada, an armed fleet of 130 warships, to England. The English ships were faster and soon caught up with the armada and defeated it. The defeat established England as a major sea power.

Elizabeth was not an absolute monarch. When Elizabeth needed money from the English treasury to fight the Spanish Armada, she needed Parliament's approval. The English **Parliament** could disapprove laws or taxes that the monarch wanted.

**?** What were some of Elizabeth's accomplishments as the queen of England?

> **Parliament**
> (pär′lə-mənt)
>
> a national governing body that represents the people and has the highest law-making powers in the nation.

## The English Civil War

Elizabeth died in 1603. The crown passed to King James of Scotland. His son, Charles I became king of England in 1625. Charles dismissed Parliament whenever it refused his requests. And he persecuted the Puritans—strict Protestants who wanted a simpler form of worship than the Church of England had. In 1628, Parliament refused to approve Charles's request for more money unless he signed the Petition of Right. This petition made it illegal for the king to imprison citizens, such as the Puritans, for no reason. Charles signed the petition. But he dismissed Parliament and ruled alone for 11 years.

*Summary continues on next page*

In 1642, Puritans and merchants helped Parliament take control of the army and the central government. Church leaders and nobles supported Charles. Civil War broke out. The Puritan leader Oliver Cromwell led Parliament's army to victory. In 1649, Charles was accused of trying to "overthrow the rights and liberties of this people." Parliament found Charles guilty and put him to death.

For four years, Cromwell and a Puritan-led Parliament ran the nation. The leaders declared the nation a **commonwealth**. But in 1653, Cromwell dismissed Parliament and ended the commonwealth. He formed a new government called the Protectorate and set himself up as the Lord Protector. Cromwell ruled like a military dictator. He forced strict Puritan values upon the people. Cromwell died in 1658, and Parliament took back control of the government in 1659.

**?** Why did Charles I and Parliament quarrel?

## The Glorious Revolution

Parliament invited Charles II, the son of Charles I, to become king in 1660. Power was more evenly divided between the ruler and Parliament. Charles II died in 1685 and his Catholic brother, James II, became king. But Parliament did not want another Catholic ruler. Instead, Parliament invited James's Protestant daughter, Mary, and her Protestant husband, William of Orange, to become king and queen. William of Orange arrived in England with an army. James II gave up the crown without putting up a fight. This event is known as the Glorious Revolution because power changed hands without bloodshed.

William and Mary became the rulers of England in 1689. They had to accept the English Bill of Rights, which limited the power of the monarchy. The English Bill of Rights gave Parliament direct political power over the government of England. This legal limiting of the monarch's power made England a **constitutional monarchy**.

**?** What was the Glorious Revolution, and why was it so named?

**commonwealth**
(kŏm′ən-wĕlth′)
a nation ruled by the people

**constitutional monarchy**
(kŏn′stĭ-too′shə-nəl mŏn′ər-kē)
a monarchy in which the powers of the ruler are limited to those granted by the constitution and the nation's laws

CHAPTER 17

# Lesson 3 Preview
## European Expansion

(*Across the Centuries* pp. 464–470)

### Colonies in the Americas

|  | Colony Location | Colony Resources |
|---|---|---|
| **England** | North America | crops, furs |
| **France** | North America | furs |
| **Netherlands** | North America | furs |
| **Portugal** | South America | crops, metals |
| **Spain** | N. and S. America | crops, metals |

1. **Look at the graphic organizer above. Then read the following sentences and fill in the blanks.**

   a. Both England and France had colonies in _____ America.

   b. Crops and _____ were two colonial resources of Portugal and Spain.

   c. The Netherlands got _____ from its colonies in _____ America.

2. **Read the lesson title and the red and blue headings in your text, pages 464–470. Use words from those headings to fill in the lesson outline below.**

   I. Growth of the Portuguese _____

      A. Exploring the _____

      B. _____ Up Trade

   II. Expansion of the _____ Empire

      A. The Encomienda _____

      B. _____

      C. _____ and Race

   III. _____, English, and _____ Competition

      A. Trade in the _____

      B. _____ in the West

      C. _____ in the _____

# Lesson 3 Reading Strategy
## European Expansion

*(Across the Centuries* pp. 464–470)

**Cause and Effect** This reading strategy helps you understand events and why they occur. As you read, think about the factors that caused an event. Then think about what the effects of that event may be.

1. Read the section "Growth of the Portuguese Empire" on pages 465–466. Which of the following caused the Portuguese to begin exploring the seas? Circle the letter next to the best answer.

   a. They wanted to find a new sea route to the Indies.

   b. Native workers were dying on Brazilian plantations.

   c. Portugal had claimed a large part of South America.

2. Which of the following was an effect of Portuguese sea exploration? Circle the letter next to the best answer.

   a. Italian merchants controlled most of the East Indies spice trade.

   b. The Portuguese laid claim to a large area of South America.

   c. Muslims were expelled from Portugal.

3. Read the section "Expansion of the Spanish Empire" on pages 466–467. Then look at the information in the chart below. Decide whether each item is a cause or an effect of the Triangle Trade. Write a *C* next to causes and an *E* next to effects.

| | |
|---|---|
| Economic policies such as mercantilism | |
| Racism | |
| The establishment of colonies in the Americas and Africa | |
| A desire for cheap labor in the Americas | |

4. Read the section "Dutch, English, and French Competition" on pages 468–470. Write one cause of the European nations' competition for colonies in North America. Then write one effect of the competition.

   Cause: _____

   _____

   Effect: _____

   _____

# Lesson 3 Summary
## European Expansion

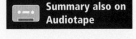
(*Across the Centuries* pp. 464–470)

**Thinking Focus:** Why did European nations establish colonies throughout the world?

## Growth of the Portuguese Empire

Europeans called India and the islands southeast of it "the East Indies." In the 1400s, the Portuguese wanted to set up a sea route to the Indies. They wanted to control trade from the East Indies, and spread the Catholic religion to new lands. By 1498, they had explored the east coast of Africa and had reached India. The Portuguese set up trading posts on the west coast of Africa, where they traded guns, knives, and cloth for African gold and ivory. The Africans also sold slaves to the Portuguese. In 1500, a Portuguese ship landed, perhaps by accident, on the east coast of South America in what is now Brazil. The Portuguese claimed a large part of South America.

In the 1530s Portuguese colonists began to set up sugar cane plantations in Brazil. Slaves from Africa were forced to work on the plantations. The exchange of goods and slaves among Africa, South America, and Europe formed a "Triangle Trade."

? Why did the Portuguese seek new trade routes to the Indies?

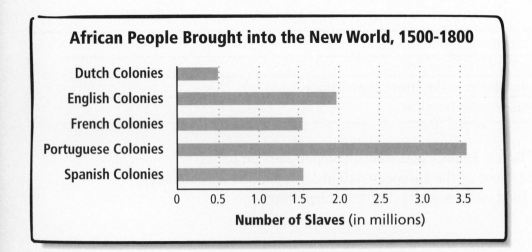

**African People Brought into the New World, 1500-1800**

| Colony | |
|---|---|
| Dutch Colonies | ~0.5 |
| English Colonies | ~2.0 |
| French Colonies | ~1.6 |
| Portuguese Colonies | ~3.5 |
| Spanish Colonies | ~1.6 |

**Number of Slaves** (in millions)

Summary continues on next page

## Expansion of the Spanish Empire

By 1550, Spain controlled Mexico, Central America, part of South America, most Caribbean islands, and part of what is now the southwestern United States. The Spanish developed the **encomienda system**. Under this system, a Spanish colonist made a group of Indians work for him. In exchange, he housed and fed the Indians and instructed them in the Catholic faith. For their part, the Indians mined and farmed the land and had to pay tribute. Many Indians died from the hard labor and Spanish-carried diseases. African slaves were brought to replace the Indians.

Spain and Portugal both followed an economic policy called **mercantilism**. Under this policy, native peoples and slaves were forced to mine the colonies' land and tend its crops. The goods were sent back to the ruling country. European colonizing and trading in slaves led to racism. Europeans came to divide the peoples of the world according to skin color.

[?] Describe the encomienda system and the policy of mercantilism.

## Dutch, English, and French Competition

Around 1600 the Dutch began taking control of Portuguese colonies and trade routes in the Eastern Hemisphere. The Dutch, English, and French founded large trading companies financed by private citizens. These companies were given government **charters**, which gave them a great deal of control over the colonies.

Then England, France and the Netherlands turned to the Atlantic coast of North America to establish colonies. In 1607, the English made a permanent settlement at Jamestown. In 1624, the Dutch founded the New Netherland colony. England and the Netherlands competed for the fur trade. In 1664, the Dutch lost New Netherland to the English. In 1608, France founded a settlement in Quebec in present-day Canada. France and England also fought battles over the fur trade. In 1763, France lost control of much of its colonial territory to Britain.

[?] Why did the Dutch, English, and French settle in North America?

---

**encomienda system**
(ĕn-kō′mē-ĕn′də sĭs təm)

a system in which a Spanish colonist received from his government the grant of a group of Indians who had to work for him. In exchange, he was entrusted to house and feed the Indians and instruct them in the Catholic faith.

**mercantilism**
(mûr′kən-tē-lĭz′əm)

a political and economic system based on setting up colonies to serve as a source of raw materials and also as a place for selling goods

**charter**
(chär′tər)

an official document created by a monarch or government that sets up a public or private company

---

# Chapter Overview
## The Enlightenment

**Fill in the blank spaces below with information from the chapter.**

**When:**
1690–1800

**Who:**
Europeans and Americans

### Dawn of a New Era

Locke publishes his "Two Treatises on Government"  —  **1690**

Diderot publishes
_____  —  **1751**

● — Declaration of Independence

● — The French Revolution

Napoleon comes to power in France  **1799**

CHAPTER 18

# Lesson 1 Preview
## A New Order of Ideals

*(Across the Centuries* pp. 476–479)

## Enlightenment Solutions

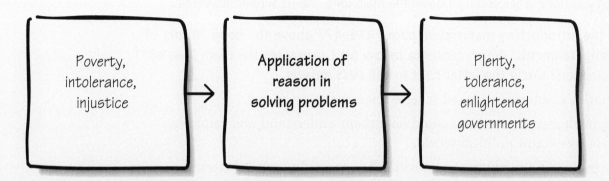

1. **Look at the graphic organizer above. Then read the following sentences and fill in the blanks.**

   a. Poverty, _____, and injustice were some of the problems facing Europeans in the 1600s and 1700s.

   b. Great thinkers believed that the application of _____ could solve problems.

2. **Look at the illustration and its caption at the bottom of page 477 in your text. Then answer the following questions:**

   a. What is the name of the artist who drew this illustration?

   _____

   b. Who is the person in the illustration and what was he famous for?

   _____

   _____

CHAPTER 18

# Lesson 1 Reading Strategy
## A New Order of Ideals

(*Across the Centuries* pp. 476–479)

**Finding the Main Idea** This reading strategy helps you organize and remember what you read. When you finish a selection, jot down the main idea and its supporting details.

1. **Read the introductory material on pages 476–477 above the head "Roots of the Enlightenment." Which sentence below best expresses the main idea of the selection? Circle the letter next to the best answer.**

   a. Charles Coulomb invented several scientific instruments.

   b. People hoped that reason could help them understand and improve their social and political world.

   c. By using reason, governments could be changed to work better.

2. **Which sentences in question 1, if any, are supporting details for the main idea? Write a *D* next to your choice(s).**

3. **Read the section "European Philosophers" on pages 477–478. Then supply two details to the chart below that support the main idea.**

| Main Idea | Supporting Details |
|---|---|
| European thinkers hoped they could use reason to achieve progress in areas other than the sciences. | 1. _____<br>2. _____ |

4. **Read the section "New Ideas about Government" on page 479. Write the main idea of the selection and two supporting details.**

   Main Idea: _____

   _____

   Supporting Details: _____

   _____

# Lesson 1 Summary
## A New Order of Ideals

(*Across the Centuries* pp. 476–479)

Summary also on Audiotape

---

**Thinking Focus:** How did the Age of Enlightenment reflect a spirit of optimism?

## Roots of the Enlightenment

During the Renaissance, philosophers developed the idea of humanism. Humanists believed in individualism—the idea that each person has value and the ability to achieve.

By the 1700s, European philosophers and scientists believed that **reason** was the key to understanding the world and creating a perfect society. They felt that individuals had the power to change society. Many people believed that knowledge and reason could free the world of wrong ideas and bring an end to injustice and poverty. Because of this belief in new possibilities, the 1700s became known as the **Age of Enlightenment.**

[?] How did the idea of individualism lead to the Enlightenment?

## European Philosophers

European thinkers during the 1600s and 1700s hoped they could use reason to change society. These thinkers were called **philosophes**, the French word for philosophers. The philosophes wanted to give power to individuals and spread scientific knowledge. They also wanted to increase religious tolerance. The most famous philosophe was a Frenchman who used the pen name Voltaire.

[?] What changes did the philosophes want to make in society?

**reason**
(rē´zən)
the ability to think logically

**Age of Enlightenment**
(āj ŭv ĕn-līt´n-mənt)
a movement in Europe and America in the 1700s that used human reason to understand ideas and problems in society

**philosophe**
(fē´lə-zôf´)
a European thinker or writer of the 1700s

*Summary continues on next page*

# New Ideas about Government

John Locke of England, Baron de Montesquieu of France, and Jean-Jacques Rousseau of Switzerland were three thinkers who worked on finding a perfect form of government. They all agreed that the goal of a government should be to improve life for its people.

Locke wrote that government was a **contract** between the people and their ruler. People would allow the ruler power if he or she ruled fairly and protected each person's **natural rights**. People could break the contract and overthrow the ruler if he or she was unfair.

Montesquieu felt that the power of the ruler should be limited. He suggested limiting the ruler's power by dividing the government into three equal branches—legislative, executive, and judicial.

Rousseau wanted to limit the power of the ruler even more. He said that the people should participate directly in the government. Like Locke, he also felt that government was a contract and that people could break the contract if the government wasn't serving their needs.

**contract**
(kŏn´trăckt´)

an agreement between two or more individuals or groups

**natural rights**
(năch´ər-əl rīt)

rights that many people believed all people should have including life, liberty, and the right to own property

## Philosophies of Government

|  | Locke | Montesquieu | Rousseau |
|---|---|---|---|
| Government should respect the rights of the people. | X | X | X |
| A contract exists between the people and the ruler. | X |  | X |
| The power of government should be limited. |  | X | X |
| People should participate directly in the government. |  |  | X |

**?** How were Locke, Montesquieu, and Rousseau alike and different in their philosophies of government?

CHAPTER 18

# Lesson 2 Preview
## Ideas in Action

*(Across the Centuries pp. 480–485)*

### Ideals of the Enlightenment

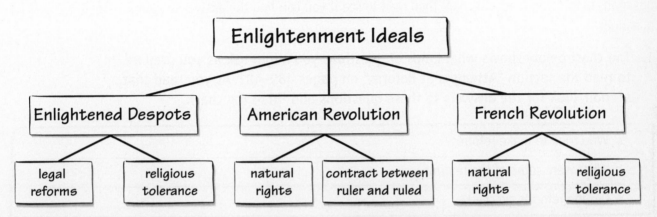

1. **Look at the graphic organizer above. Then read the following sentences and fill in the blanks.**

   a. Enlightened _____ made legal reforms and tried to practice religious tolerance.

   b. Key ideas of the American Revolution included _____ rights and a contract between the _____ and the ruled.

   c. Natural rights and _____ tolerance were two results of the _____ Revolution.

2. **Look at the pictures in this lesson, then focus on the picture at the bottom of page 483. Write down your thoughts about what the ideas of the Enlightenment might have to do with this picture.**

   _____

   _____

   _____

   _____

   _____

   _____

CHAPTER 18

# Lesson 2 Reading Strategy
## Ideas in Action

(*Across the Centuries* pp. 480–485)

**Self-Question** This reading strategy helps you stay focused on what you read. Ask yourself questions before you read a section. Then read to see if you can find the answer to your questions.

1. **The chart below shows what kinds of questions you might ask as you prepare to read the section "Attempts at Reform" on pages 480–481. As you read that section, look for the answers to these questions and fill in the chart.**

   a. Who tried to make reforms? _____

   b. What were some of the reforms? _____

   c. Did the reforms succeed? _____

2. **Read the section heading "Influences in America" and the first paragraph that follows on page 482. Which question below would you expect to have answered by reading the section? Circle the letter next to the best answer.**

   **a.** Who was Benjamin Franklin's favorite philosopher?

   **b.** How were Enlightenment ideas put into action in France?

   **c.** How were Enlightenment ideas put into action in North America?

3. **Read the section "Influences in America" on page 482 to see if the question you chose was answered. If it was, write the answer to the question**

   _____

   _____

4. **Read the heading "The French Revolution" and the smaller headings that follow on pages 482–485. Write a question in the space below that you expect to have answered as you read the section.**

   _____

   _____

   **Read the section and look for the answer to your question. Write your answer in the space below.**

   _____

   _____

# Lesson 2 Summary
## Ideas in Action

(*Across the Centuries* pp. 480–485)

---

**Thinking Focus:** How did the ideas of the Enlightenment affect governments in Europe and America?

---

## Attempts at Reform

During the late 1700s, some European rulers tried to follow some Enlightenment ideals. They were all-powerful monarchs, or despots. This means they made all decisions concerning the government and the running of the country. But because they were trying to improve the lives of their people, they were called **enlightened despots.**

Some rulers made good changes. For example, Joseph II of Austria abolished serfdom and let peasants own land. He also taxed all classes equally and gave religious freedom to all. But the nobles of Austria, who had held the land, felt that changes could weaken their power. Rulers needed the nobles' support. Since the nobles did not support the reforms, many changes were ended after the monarch's death.

? Why were the reforms of enlightened despots largely unsuccessful?

> **enlightened despot**
> (ĕn-līt′nd dĕs′pət)
> a European ruler of the 1700s who was all-powerful but who tried to follow Enlightenment ideals, such as tolerance and freedom

## Influences in America

In 1776, colonial leaders drafted a Declaration of Independence. This document demanded freedom from British rule. The idea of declaring independence comes from Locke's belief that people have the right to dissolve their contract with an unfair ruler. The Declaration of Independence also included Locke's idea of natural rights.

? How does the Declaration of Independence reflect the influence of Enlightenment thinkers?

*Summary continues on next page*

# The French Revolution

In 1787, the poor in France suffered from hunger, high taxes, and unemployment. Yet King Louis XVI called a meeting of the government to raise taxes. The common people, called the Third Estate, were angry that they had almost no power in government and tired of having to pay the most taxes. In June 1789, they formed the National Assembly. The Assembly called for a constitutional monarchy under which the people were more fairly taxed. Louis XVI needed money, so he gave in to their demands.

In July, 1789, Louis XVI placed troops outside Paris. The people feared he planned to take away the Assembly's power. On July 14, a crowd overran a prison called the Bastille. They freed the prisoners. This started the French Revolution.

In August 1789, the Assembly wrote a new constitution. The Assembly established a constitutional monarchy. It also granted religious freedom to Protestants and Jews.

In 1792, Louis XVI was caught plotting to overthrow the new government. He was beheaded. France became a republic. But a violent period known as the Reign of Terror followed. In 1799, General Napoleon Bonaparte seized control of the government and the revolution came to an end.

**?** How are the reforms that took place during the French Revolution representative of Enlightenment ideals?

CHAPTER 18

# Lesson 3 Preview
## Economic Changes

(*Across the Centuries* pp. 490–493)

## The Agricultural and Industrial Revolutions

|  | Elements | Positives | Negatives |
|---|---|---|---|
| **Agricultural Revolution** | new tools and crops, enclosure | produced more food with less labor | displaced small farmers |
| **Industrial Revolution** | new machines, division of labor | provided jobs and made goods efficiently | caused poor working and living conditions |

1. **Look at the graphic organizer above. Then read the following sentences and fill in the blanks.**

   a. One of the positive results of the _____ Revolution was that more food was produced with less labor.

   b. One of the negative results of the Industrial _____ was _____ working and living conditions.

   c. New tools and machines were elements of both the _____ and the _____ revolutions.

2. **Read the lesson title and the red and blue headings in your text on pages 490 to 493. Use words from those headings to fill in the lesson outline below.**

   Economic Changes

   I. The Agricultural _____

      A. _____ Rotation

      B. _____ Tools

      C. _____

   II. The _____ Revolution

      A. New _____

      B. Capital and _____

      C. _____ of _____

CHAPTER 18

# Lesson 3 Reading Strategy
## Economic Changes

(Across the Centuries pp. 490–493)

**Using the Visuals** This reading strategy helps you use photographs, maps, charts, and illustrations to help you understand what you read. As you read, be sure to study the visuals and carefully read the captions.

1. **Look at the picture on page 490 and read the caption. What can you conclude from the picture and caption? Circle the letter next to the best answer.**

   a. Gleaners used expensive farm machines.

   b. Gleaners were poor peasants.

   c. Gleaners didn't want to work hard.

2. **Look at the picture of the seed drill on page 491 and read the caption. What moved the seed drill along the field? Circle the letter next to the best answer.**

   a. horses

   b. men

   c. a gasoline engine

3. **Look at the chart "Specialization of Labor" on page 492 and read the caption. Use the chart and the caption to fill in the chart below.**

| | |
|---|---|
| a. How many hours did it take one person doing each step to make one pair of shoes? | |
| b. How many hours did it take five people each doing only one step to make eight pairs of shoes? | |
| c. What is eliminated in the five-person process? | |

4. **Use your answers in the chart to answer the following question. Does specialization of labor make shoemaking faster and more efficient? Explain your answer.**

_____

_____

_____

# Lesson 3 Summary
## Economic Changes

(*Across the Centuries* pp. 490–493)

**Thinking Focus:** How did the agricultural and industrial revolutions change life in Britain during the 1700s?

## The Agricultural Revolution

By the end of the 1700s, British farmers were learning new ways to farm. New farming ideas helped farmers grow more food. New ways of growing food led to a different life for many people and was called an **agricultural revolution**.

In medieval Britain, farmers used a three-field crop-growing system. Each year they would plant crops in two fields. The third field was left unplanted so the soil could rest. The next year they would switch the crops they planted in each of the fields. Under this system of **crop rotation**, a farmer was not able to use all of his land. One field was always unused.

In the 1600s, British farmers started to change the crop rotation system. They grew new crops, such as turnips or clover, in the field that had been resting. These crops improved the soil and made it more fertile. The new system allowed farmers to grow more crops. New farm tools also made farming more productive.

In the 1600s and 1700s wealthy landowners bought up much of the unfenced fields that peasants had used for growing their grain. The new owners fenced in this land. This was known as **enclosure**. Landowners introduced new farming methods and increased the amount of food that could be produced on the same amount of land. Peasants lost land because of enclosure. So, many peasants went to the cities to look for work.

**?** What developments changed agriculture in Britain?

**agricultural revolution**
(ăg-rĭ-kŭl′chər-əl rĕv′ə-lōō´-shən)

a series of developments in Europe during the 1700s that improved farming methods and increased crop production

**crop rotation**
(krŏp rō-tā′shən)

the planting of crops in different fields in alternate years to keep soil fertile

**enclosure**
(ĕn-klō′zhər)

the fencing in of common land to form larger properties in Britain during the 1700s

*Summary continues on next page*

# The Industrial Revolution

As Britain's population grew, the demand for goods also increased. People who made goods by hand could not keep up with the demand. New machines were invented that made goods faster and more cheaply. These changes in how goods were manufactured were called an **industrial revolution**.

Many of the new inventions of the 1700s changed the cloth industry. One new invention was the spinning jenny, which spun fibers into thread much more quickly than the old spinning wheels. Another new machine was the steam-powered loom. Because of inventions like these, England greatly increased its production of cloth.

Capital and labor, or money and workers, were both important in the industrial revolution. **Capitalists** invested money in the new industries to help them grow. The new factories needed workers to run the machines. Landless peasants who came to the cities found work in the factories. Conditions in factories were not good. Workers, including young children, worked long hours, and unsafe machines sometimes caused terrible accidents.

**?** What conditions contributed to the growth of industry in the late 1700s?

**industrial revolution**
(ĭn-dŭs′trē-əl rĕv′ə-lōō′shən)

the improvements in industry that began in Britain during the 18th century

**capitalist**
(kăp′ĭ-tl-ĭst)

a person who invests money, or capital, in business

CHAPTER 18

# Lesson 4 Preview
## After the American Revolution

*(Across the Centuries pp. 497–500)*

### Enlightenment Ideas Affect the United States

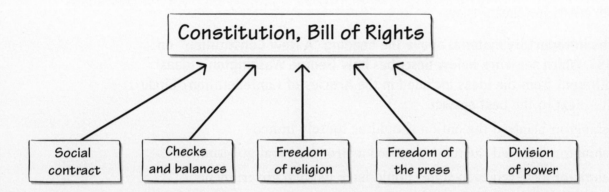

1. **Look at the graphic organizer above. Then read the following sentences and fill in the blanks.**

   a. The writers of the Constitution built in a system of checks and

   _____.

   b. Division of _____ is an important feature of the Constitution.

   c. The Bill of Rights calls for freedom of the press and freedom of

   _____.

2. **Look through the lesson on pages 497 to 500 in your text for the photos of three U.S. government buildings.**

   a. Write down the page number where the photos appear.

   _____

   b. Write down the names of the three buildings.

   _____

   _____

   _____

CHAPTER 18

# Lesson 4 Reading Strategy
## After the American Revolution

(*Across the Centuries* pp. 497–500)

**Compare and Contrast** This reading strategy helps you understand how events are similar and different. As you read about historical events, think about how they compare and contrast with events you already know.

1. Read the introductory material above the heading "A New Constitution" on page 497. Which sentence below describes how George Washington's ideas were different from the ideas included in the Articles of Confederation? Circle the letter next to the best answer.

    a. Washington believed the nation should be loosely united.

    b. Washington believed the nation needed a strong central government.

    c. Washington believed each state should have its own government.

2. Read the section "A New Constitution" on pages 497–498. Write two sentences explaining ways in which the ideas of the Constitution are similar to the ideas of the philosophes.

    _____

    _____

3. Read the section "Around the World in 1790" on page 500. Then look at the chart below. Compare and contrast the listed countries by placing an *X* in the column that describes the government of each country listed below.

| | Government by the People | Government by a Ruler |
|---|---|---|
| France | | |
| Japan | | |
| Mexico | | |
| United States | | |
| India | | |

Reading Support Resources

# Lesson 4 Summary
## After the American Revolution

(*Across the Centuries* pp. 497–500)

**Thinking Focus:** What Enlightenment ideals did the founders of the government of the United States share with the philosophes?

## A New Constitution

After the North American colonists overthrew Britain's authority, government in the new nation was based on the Articles of Confederation. But the Articles, which were approved in 1777, only loosely united the 13 states. Each state was like its own separate country, with its own government, army, trade, and currency. Many people felt that the nation needed to work out away to bring the states into a stronger unit. In 1787, the leaders of the United States wrote a Constitution that guaranteed a strong central government. The Constitution also spelled out the natural rights of the people. The Enlightenment ideals of the philosophes influenced the Constitution. Like the philosophes Locke and Rousseau, Americans believed that government was a social contract between the people and their ruler.

The new Constitution also made sure that no part of the government could become too powerful. This idea, too, came from the Enlightenment. The philosophe Montesquieu wrote that "power should be a check to power." To keep power balanced, the Constitution calls for three branches of power in the government. These branches are the legislative (Congress), executive (President), and judicial (Supreme Court). The writers of the Constitution wanted the three branches to serve as a system of **checks and balances**. This system would make sure that power was balanced. No branch would be more powerful than another.

[?] What ideas in the Constitution are similar to the ideals of the philosophes?

**checks and balances**
(chĕks ənd băl'əns-əz)

the system of keeping a balance of power between various branches of government

*Summary continues on next page*

## Checks and Balances in the Three Branches of Government

**Executive**

The President can veto, or refuse to pass, bills passed by Congress.

**Legislative**

Congress can pass a bill that has been vetoed by the President if they can pass it again with a two-thirds vote.

**Judicial**

Supreme Court can cancel laws that have been passed by Congress if the laws are judged to be in conflict with the Constitution.

# Around the World in 1790

In 1790, shortly after the United States won its independence, Britain was the largest and most powerful empire in the world. The trade agreements Britain made between itself and its colonies around the world were made so that Britain benefited the most.

In China, Emperor Qianlong ruled a large, rich empire. But the empire was closed to outside influences and threats. In Japan, the powerful Tokugawa clan ruled. In Spanish-held America, people worked in mines and on ranches that were owned by the Spanish.

With the adoption of the U.S. Constitution in 1790, the Americans did something completely new. They chose a system of government based on Enlightenment ideals and lessons from history. Most of the other people of the world still had no voice in government. The American ideas of equal rights, freedom of speech and belief, and democratic decision making by the people would have seemed impossible to them.

? What was happening in the United States at this time that was so unusual?